plays 1

Return stock

WORDPLAYS

Series editor: Alan Durband

Wordplays 1

We Shall Never Die *Dave Sheasby*
The Tree Machine *Mandy Alexander*
The Awful Billy Smiff *Brian Jacques*
Darren's Conker *Anne Pickles*
Politics and Terror *Willy Russell*
All Friends Together *Tim Shields*

Wordplays 2

The Killer Cave *Alan England*
The Dividing Fence *Peter Terson*
Get Well Soon *Ken Campbell*
What are We Going to do Now? *Alan Bleasdale*
Gone to Jesus *Chris Bond*
Breaking Out *George Friel*

Other drama anthologies edited by Alan Durband

Playbill One
Playbill Two

Wordplays 1

Six short modern plays

Edited by Alan Durband

Stanley Thornes (Publishers) Ltd

First published in 1982 by Hutchinson Education
Reprinted in 1984, 1986

Reprinted in 1991 by
Stanley Thornes (Publishers) Ltd
Old Station Drive
Leckhampton
CHELTENHAM GL53 0DN
England

British Library Cataloguing in Publication Data
Wordplays

1. College and school drama
2. One-act plays, English
3. English drama – 20th century
I. Durband, Alan
822'.041'08   PN6120.A4

ISBN 0 7487 1013 2

Printed and bound in Great Britain at Courier International Limited, Tiptree, Essex.

Contents

To
Audrey, Len and Godfrey
in the first place

Introduction

Drama in schools
Most large secondary schools have a drama department, or at least a drama specialist. Smaller schools usually have an English teacher with a drama bias. Today, drama has a recognized place in the school curriculum.

This has not always been so.

Drama is a relatively new school subject. Some older teachers still regard it with suspicion, perhaps because they remember the days when the only plays to be read in school were those of Shakespeare – and even Shakespeare's plays were heavily cut to make them suitable for young readers.

Nobody ever studied the plays that were filling the theatres of their day. They were not regarded as suitable material, either for pleasure reading or examinations.

Eventually, in the 1920s, a publisher risked an anthology of one-act plays. He hoped that schools would not object to their popular appeal. The editor explained in his preface that the end justified the means – he hoped that his readers would eventually move on to like Shakespeare. He had to be very cautious in case he was accused of making life too easy for teachers and pupils.

To his surprise, the experimental volume sold very well, and fifty years later it is still in print. Many other anthologies have followed – collections of short 'curtain raisers' from the theatre (when these were popular), and later 'one-acters' which were mostly written to meet the needs of amateur dramatic societies.

This collection of short plays – *Wordplays* – is not just another anthology in this long tradition.

It really belongs to another story.

The decline of the theatre

Between the two world wars, the professional theatre went into decline. Many theatres closed down. Others were converted into cinemas. Talented playwrights were rare, and though there were still many ardent theatre-goers, they tended to be very middle-class and settled in their tastes.

The impact of television seemed to be the final blow.

Even more theatres closed down, or were turned this time into Bingo Halls. Theatres simply could not pay their way. They seemed to be outdated museum-pieces, with no purpose and no future. It was possible to buy a fully-equipped theatre for the price of a semi-detached house. Nobody wanted to buy.

The great revival

And yet today the theatre is very much alive. New ones are being built and old ones restored.

The revival dates back to the early 1950s, when the English Stage Society took over the Royal Court Theatre in Sloane Square, London. Its policy was to experiment, and to encourage new playwrights.

Its first and greatest success changed the entire

direction of modern theatre. John Osborne's *Look Back in Anger* (1956) started a new wave of interest in drama. Young writers from all walks of life were inspired to write plays with entirely new subjects and in experimental ways. In place of the 'Who's for Tennis?' kinds of play (so-called because they always seemed to be about middle-class people) they wrote what the critics called 'kitchen sink' dramas – down-to-earth plays involving working-class people and their daily lives.

Abolition of censorship

Theatre took on a social conscience, and it tackled subjects which challenged the existing laws.

In those days, all plays were subject to censorship, and every playscript had to be passed by the Lord Chancellor. He would cut out words or situations which he thought were offensive, or ban an entire play. But so vigorous was the new thrust in the theatre that the Lord Chancellor and his office were swept away, and playwrights were free to write the kind of plays which modern audiences wanted to see.

Subsidy

At the same time, financial aid came to the rescue of theatres, by way of grants from the central government (through the Arts Council), and from many local authorities (through Regional Arts Associations and the funding of civic theatres).

Theatres no longer had to choose plays purely to make money. They could try out new ideas, and take a few risks. Many began to add a playwright to their payroll, ensuring a constant flow of new work, often reflecting local interests and involving the community as a whole.

Parliament even passed a Theatres Act, making it difficult to demolish a theatre without a very good reason.

Drama in education

This upsurge of interest in the professional theatre had an influence on drama in schools.

The range of plays available in school editions widened enormously. Examining Boards began to choose contemporary plays for close study. In some areas, local authorities set up TIE (Theatre-in-Education) teams, consisting of professional actors, to visit schools with specially-written programmes. Sometimes they perform plays, sometimes they 'make a play' on the spot, and involve the audience in choosing a theme and performing the parts.

Improvised drama

Some gifted drama teachers also began to work in a totally new area. They found that playscripts were unnecessary. The ideas for entire plays, and the words themselves, came from the pupils. Often they expressed their feelings in movement and dance.

'Improvised drama' is now central to any drama course in schools, and teachers with special training are now appointed to drama departments. When pupils talk about 'drama', they may mean this kind of activity, and not the reading of scripts.

And that is where we are today.

We have a lively professional theatre, bursting with energy, new plays, and new playwrights. And we have equally lively drama departments in schools, some-times working without any scripts at all.

Although the two forms of drama are closely related, there is a danger that they could develop so separately that their common origin becomes forgotten.

Perhaps the answer is, once again, the drama anthology. This is where *Wordplays* come into the story.

Wordplays

Each play is, in one way or another, a good example of drama in the 1980s. All the playwrights are writing in a contemporary style, and their techniques belong to the mainstream of dramatic thinking.

In spite of this, they should be readable by secondary pupils of all ages from 11 onwards, because the language is simple and most speeches are short. The themes throughout are strong, and should lead to plenty of comment and discussion.

The **words** are provided. How you **play** them is a matter of interpretation.

Wordplays 1

The first two plays are *documentaries*. Dave Sheasby wrote *We Shall Never Die* for a Radio Sheffield schools' series.

Material for the play came from history. In 1832, there was a mining disaster at Silkstone Colliery. A flash flood swept through the underground tunnels, and many children were drowned at their work. They were 'trappers'. Their job was to open and close doors as part of the ventilation system of the colliery. A monu-ment was erected in their memory in the village of

Silkstone, which is near Sheffield, and it is still there today.

The incident itself would have been nothing more than a memory in stone if Dave Sheasby had not done some research and brought it back to life in a play. Now the experience of being a trapper can be relived, and the day of disaster can be re-enacted.

This play has the longest speeches in the anthology. If it is a problem, then a full production with movement and props might be best avoided. Instead, the play could be tape-recorded, or read by a group of readers sitting or standing with scripts in their hands – for example, at a school assembly, on the platform.

If it isn't a problem, then an acted version could be attempted. A Sheffield middle-school performed the play in public, guided by a teacher. They used the school hall, with the action taking place round the walls and the audience sitting in the middle, like this:

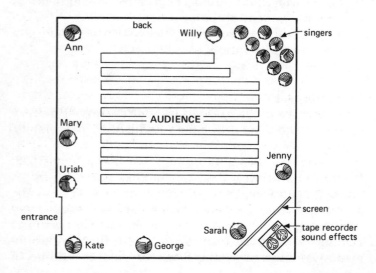

The 'trappers' sat on simple boxes. The windows were blacked out and a spotlight was used to pick out each speaker in turn. Costumes were very basic: modern clothes with simple extras such as scarves and caps for the boys, and long skirts for the girls. Pit-tubs could be anything from converted prams to large cardboard boxes on wheels. A simple sound-effect tape adds atmosphere to the play, especially during the storm scene. The narrator could be the class teacher or a good reader. He or she would take a central place, and as the story unfolds, the trappers could be picked out by the spotlight and followed to their workplaces. Coal tubs could circle the audience and stop at the various bases as the story requires.

The second documentary – *The Tree Machine* by Mandy Alexander – is an example of how improvised drama and scripted drama are closely related.

The play grew out of a history lesson. The class was studying the social life of the nineteenth century, which sounds as though it might have been rather dull. But instead of copying down notes about the major people and events of the period, the class acted them out. One topic chosen was the misuse of child labour, and the dreadful working conditions of chimney sweeps in the days when climbing boys were used to loosen the soot.

Teacher and class together worked out how they would dramatize the story, choosing the main characters and deciding on the number of scenes. Then, without scripts, they performed a version of *The Tree Machine* in the classroom. The cast enjoyed this so much that they asked the teacher to 'write it up'. This she did, and many of the speeches are those which were successful in the improvised version. The scripted version was then performed several times more, for the benefit of other classes in the school. Here again, the play can be used like a radio play and tape-recorded, or it can be given full-scale production using the usual furniture found in school.

With this play as an example, others can be devised by similar methods. The documents of history are an inexhaustible supply of suitable material.

Plays 3 and 4 in the anthology are school and classroom based, so there are no production problems.

The Awful Billy Smiff by Brian Jacques is in two parts.

In the first, we are introduced to Billy by means of his reputation. His teachers tell a new recruit to the profession of the horrors that await her in 2C. Our interest is aroused. Billy Smiff is a legend in his own time: but can he really be so Awful?

In the second scene, we see him in action. He has several clever little tricks to wear Miss Crampton down, but in the first round of the contest she manages to hold her own.

When she embarks on the lesson itself, the cracks start to appear. Following the rules of her training, Miss Crampton refuses to let Billy dominate the classroom. She gives other children a share of her attention. But Billy will not be put down. Eventually she relents – with fatal results. In an atmosphere of rising tension, poor Miss Crampton's inevitable fate is sealed.

The Awful Billy Smiff wins again!

The staffroom scene can be played 'out front', assuming the classroom is set out conventionally with rows of desks facing the blackboard. A few easy chairs would suggest the atmosphere, but it would do just as well if the teachers were simply grouped around a table, drinking tea or collecting registers.

Once the action transfers to the classroom, the play almost performs itself. The main challenge lies with the actor who plays Billy Smiff (a girls' school version would require a change of name). He has to sustain a sense of excitement. In dramatic terms, he is responsible for building up the play towards an expected climax. The joke, of course, is that Billy's punch-line is the exact reverse – a typical example of his famous Awfulness. The play's success will depend a great deal on 'timing'.

Darren's Conker by Anne Pickles is another classroom-based comedy which can be brought to life with very little trouble. (The introductory speeches of the spacemen can be pre-recorded, so they don't have to appear in their spaceship.)

For a public production, on a school stage for example, two settings are suggested. One uses a minimum number of desks and actors:

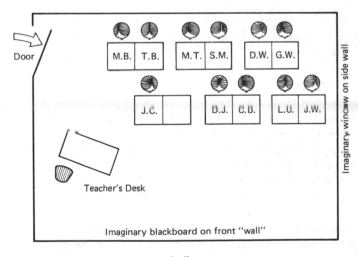

Door

M.B. | T.B.   M.T. | S.M.   D.W. | G.W.

Imaginary window on side wall

J.C.   D.J. | C.D.   L.U. | J.W.

Teacher's Desk

Imaginary blackboard on front "wall"

Audience

To use 'extras' (non-speakers) who could give atmosphere to the play by behaving naturally as pupils, then this arrangement would be better:

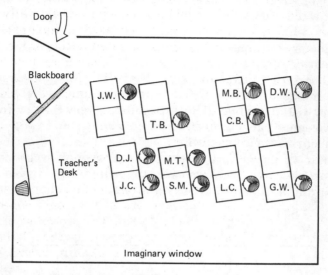

Audience

The Leader's language is really up to the actor who plays the part. The nonsense words in the script will do the job, but any kind of odd noises and squeaks will work just as well. Just imagine a foreign radio station late at night with lots of interference, and invent a similar kind of rubbish language.

Play 5, *Politics and Terror* by Willy Russell, isn't set in a classroom, but the characters have probably just escaped from one.

Classrooms have their forms of warfare, as we have seen. Street corners and wastelands have them, too. All kinds of battles are fought there by children of cunning and skill. They are never taught how to manipulate each other – the art seems to pass down the generations like an instinct.

Notice Willy Russell's marvellous gift – what we call 'an ear for dialogue'. When his characters speak, we feel we have heard the words before because they have such a natural sound. All day long we listen to this natural speech going on around us: it is the language of people using words and phrases unaffectedly. Good dialogue captures this 'real' sound. Conversations seem like ordinary talk written down. It sounds very easy to do, but in practice it is not so simple.

Politics and Terror is a brilliant example of children's everyday speech as it is used to cope with an everyday situation. In performance, the challenge lies in keeping this natural quality. The actors must appear to be talking together, not reciting lines. In improvised drama, this would be no problem. The words would come straight from the performers' mouths – though the words wouldn't flow with anything like the accuracy captured in the *Politics and Terror* script. A good performance, however, will sound like an improvisation. . . .

Finally, Play 6. Tim Shields' *All Friends Together* is a good example of the short play.

It isn't in one act, as in days gone by. Film and television have made us familiar with dramatic stories told in short scenes. Notice how often scenes can change in a typical TV play: sometimes the drama unfolds by camera shots alone, or dialogue cut down to single words or phrases. And there is no need to worry about 'sets' for each scene. Modern audiences are used to using their imagination. Acting areas will do just as well to represent living rooms and bedrooms.

The party scene needs some skill in management. In

the professional theatre, a producer would work out all the movements in advance, to make sure all speakers can be heard and clearly seen in a crowd. In the classroom or school hall, it is worth planning where everyone should be, and rehearsing the difficult sections carefully.

Make-up would be helpful in this play. Iris could be rather pale and drab. Her parents could be somewhat exaggerated – they are larger-than-life parents anyway. So, too, could the guests. They all look alike, and the similarities could be given extra stress. Siri, on the other hand, should look like Iris in size and shape, but make-up should give her extra vitality. Attention to eyes and cheeks would achieve this. To keep the style consistent, the postman, though a minor part, should look more like a caricature than the real thing.

Before embarking on a production, everyone should agree on an interpretation. What is the purpose of the play? There is plenty of discussion material here.

This is another feature of scripted drama. Though the words always stay the same, the way in which they are delivered is a matter for decision.

The playwrights

Dave Sheasby is a local radio producer with the BBC. A native of Sheffield, where he still works, he has written a number of radio plays and a stage play for the Crucible Studio Theatre. He is also a writer of short stories.

Mandy Alexander is a teacher from Merseyside, and a graduate of Leicester University. Trained in English and History, she now teaches English and Drama at a Birkenhead school.

Brian Jacques is currently Resident Playwright at

the Everyman Theatre, Liverpool. He has had many careers in his time. Nowadays, he concentrates on cabaret performances, local radio programmes and the theatre.

Anne Pickles trained as an actress, but after eight years in the professional theatre she took up teaching. During a year's secondment to Radio Sheffield she wrote and produced programmes for schools. She has three children of her own.

Willy Russell is the author of many highly successful theatre and TV plays – *John, Paul, George, Ringo and Bert*, *Breezeblock Park*, *Stags and Hens*, and latterly *Educating Rita*, which is soon to be filmed. He is currently co-Artistic Director of the Playhouse Theatre, Liverpool.

Tim Shields was born in Dorset. A graduate of Manchester University Drama Department, he has been a Student Fellow in Playwrighting at UCLA, California, and Resident Dramatist at the Octagon Theatre, Bolton. He writes for theatre, film and TV from his base in Scotland.

Acknowledgements

For permission to publish the plays in this volume, the editor is grateful to the following authors and their agents: Dave Sheasby and Radio Sheffield for *We Shall Never Die*; Mandy Alexander for *The Tree Machine*; Brian Jacques for *The Awful Billy Smiff**; Anne Pickles and Radio Sheffield for *Darren's Conker*; Willy Russell and Margaret Ramsay Ltd for *Politics and Terror**; Tim Shields for *All Friends Together**.

*No public performance of these plays may be given without a licence. Applications should be made either to the authors or their agents.

We Shall Never Die

Dave Sheasby

Characters
Narrator
Ann Moss
Elizabeth Moss
George Burkinshaw
Jenny Burkinshaw
Willy Price   trappers
Kate Palmer   in a coal-mine
James Walker
Uriah Jubb
Mary Jubb
Sarah Gooder
Mr Harmsworth   pit manager
First Miner
Second Miner
Mr Teasdale   miner
Queen Victoria
Mrs Price   Willy's mother

We Shall Never Die

Song: [*To be sung by all class*]
Wallflowers, wallflowers,
Growing up so high.
We are little children
And we shall never die.

Wallflowers, wallflowers,
Growing up so high
See the petals falling,
But we shall never die.

Wallflowers, wallflowers,
Growing up so high,
We are little children
And we shall never die.

[*Miners and children enter and cross the stage during this narration*]

Narrator: Silkstone. A village near Barnsley. A pit village. The Huskar pit owned by the Clark family. Silkstone. A pit village. Long rows of dark houses. Homes of men and women and children who work to get the coal. The turning wheel of the pit beckons. Black spokes on black sky. It is a winter's morning in January 1838. The colliers on early turn thread their ways down dark streets towards the pit head. It is cold. The wind bites. And children, too, make for the pit head. Their footsteps print softly on the cold stones and are gone into the wind. The dark awaits them.

[**Elizabeth** *enters first.* **Ann** *lags behind*]

Ann: [*Calling*] Wait for me, Liz. I can't go as fast as you.

Elizabeth: Come on. We'll be late. You know the men don't like it. Hurry up, lass.

Ann: It's so cold. My toes aren't there.

Elizabeth: Course it's cold. It's always cold in January. [*Putting her arm round* **Ann**] Tell you what to do. Think of the summer and cold will go away. Think of the sun coming up over Keresforth Hill and the green grass in Stainboro' Park. And smell the breeze full of summer rain. And the trees all swishing and green. That's what I do these mornings to take the cold away.

[**George** *has entered during this speech and stands listening*]

Ann: Eh, that's all right, that is. Tell me some more, Elizabeth.

Elizabeth: Think of the evenings just after the sun's gone down. The noises in the street as you lie in bed under the cool sheets.

George: Lovely, I'm sure.

Elizabeth: Who is it?

Ann: It's George Burkinshaw. Over there.

Elizabeth: Oh, it's you, George. You do creep up on people.

George: Where do you get it all from? You never say a word at Sunday School and here you are going on about the green trees and summer rain and all that. Like a school teacher.

Elizabeth: Oh, shut up. I can say what I like. Besides it cheers up Ann, here.

Ann: What've you got George – for snap, I mean?

George: Bread and cheese today. My dad must've had a good week. 'Bread and Cheese. Yes, please.'

[*Whistle off*]

Elizabeth: Who's that then, whistling?

Ann: Willy Price, I bet. He whistles like that down below sometimes. I've heard him. His gate's next to mine.

Elizabeth: Willy. Come on. We know you're there.

Willy: [*Entering*] Hello everybody. Going my way? I say, what pretty young ladies. [*He goes up to take Elizabeth's arm*] Pray, take my arm and let me escort you underground.

Elizabeth: [*Pushing him away*] Ger off, yer daft thing.

Ann: [*Laughing*] He's all posh.

George: Yer mad devil.

Ann: Go on, do that funny voice again. I like it.

Willy: Who's this, then? 'Come on lads and lasses, down yer go. Mind yer bonces as yer go'.

Ann and **Elizabeth:** [*Laughing*] Mester Harmsworth.

Willy: Co-rrect!!

Ann: How do you manage to be so cheerful at this time?

Willy: Easy, folks, I whistle.

Ann: I don't feel cheerful at all.

Willy: Never mind, my little Ann. I'll whistle you a tune when it's grub time, later. All right? You wait for my whistle, and then you can eat.

Ann: [*Nearly crying*] I hate the dark. You don't know how I hate it.

Elizabeth: You might be lucky. I got a stub of candle yesterday from one of the men. I don't even know who it was. It was so dark. I just heard his voice and saw a bit of white face. Don't they look funny down there? The men, I mean.

Ann: Candle? Nobody ever gives me any and I daren't ask.

George: Well, it costs 'em, don't it? You know that. They have to pay for it. So they're not going to give it away, are they?

[**Willy** *whistles. They are all moving towards their exit*]

Elizabeth: Will the Whistler, that's what they ought to call you.

Willy: They do, my dear, they do.

Elizabeth: You shouldn't whistle down there, anyway. You know what the men say: they say it'll bring bad luck.

Ann: Never mind, Will. I'll wait for your tune. At least when I hear it I'll know someone's there. In the dark.

Willy: You wait for my whistle, my dear, and I'll be there.

[*They go off*]

Narrator: Away to the pit they go. The first pale light of day slips through the web of wheel in the sky, which turns and turns.

Mr Harmsworth: Come on lads and lasses, down yer go. And mind yer bonces as yer go.

Narrator: And as the day begins above, down they go, into the darkness below.

[*Sound effect of winch is effective here. The Song 'Wallflowers' is heard. Children sit at their places during the following narration*]

Narrator: Along the long shaft of the mine they take their places at their gates. They sit on little stools placed in little slits in the rock. Each child looks after a gate. Each is called a trapper. As men pass to and fro along the shaft, and as the tubs of coal go through the gate, each child must make sure that the gate is closed. Each gate has a string attached to it, and the children sit there on their stools in the dark, watching the men and the loads of coal pass through, and watching their own gates open and close. They sit there in the dark, for as long as the men work at the coal. Without the traps of air which the gates make, the mine would be more dangerous than it already is. They sit for hours in the dark, and watch and wait. Kate Palmer waits by her gate, afraid in the dark. She is only 9. She has been a trapper now for three years. Since she was 6 years old she has been coming down here and sitting on a stool in the darkness. She is still afraid of the blackness which covers her like a blanket every day of her life. Sometimes she talks to herself to keep her spirits up. She would like to sing, but dare not. Instead she prays.

Kate: Our father, which art in heaven, hallowed be thy name, thy kingdom come, Amen. My name is Kathleen Palmer, age nine years, three months, two days. I live in Back Lane Houses. I have three brothers and four sisters. Peter John, James John, Matthew John, Felicity, Victoria, Susan and Elizabeth. Our father. . . .

Narrator: Further along at the next gate, George Burkinshaw, age 12. He has been a trapper for four years now. He does not mind the dark at all. He sits on his stool and with a penknife hacks at pieces of wood which he makes into all sorts of shapes. Birds are his favourites. Big black crows he makes, with their big heads and black beaks and wicked eyes and stumpy legs. He watches them in the cornfields, and down in the dark he remembers them, and with his penknife he carves. He sometimes forgets his gate and gets into trouble.

[*Enter* **Miner** *with coal tub. Sound effects if possible*]

Miner: Now then, son. Get yer sen at it. The gate!

George: What? Oh, sorry!

Miner: Aye, I should think so. It's men's lives, you know. Tha's nowt else to do. Wha's up with you?

George: I forgets where I am sometimes.

Miner: Lucky lad. I wish I could do that. What's that there?

George: Nowt!

Miner: 'Ere, let's have a look.

George: No, honest.

Miner: Come on. Hand over. I'm bigger'n thee. And Mester Ronks'll want to know where I am. So give!

George: [*Handing it over*] It's a carving.

Miner: [*Bending head to see from the light of the candle on his hat*] Let's get me candle on it. Now let's see. Ah, it's all right, that. A crow, in't it?

George: Yes.

Miner: Aye. I can see it. Yer've got it off all right. I can see that. Look at that beak. Nasty things, aren't they? Muck heap birds, I calls 'em. Eat owt.

George: They don't. They only eat in the fields. They're very choosy, tha knows.

Miner: Oh aye. Know a bit about 'em, do yer?

George: Aye, a bit.

Miner: I see. Well now, just you watch yer gate. Carver or not, watch yer gate. Here, take it. [*Takes* *candle out of his pocket*] And here's a bit o' candle. Only a bit mind. It costs, yer know, that.

George: Thanks very much.

Miner: I don't know how you can see to fiddle about with that in this dark. I'm off. Think on. Yer gate! [*He goes off*]

George: I will, honest. Oh, and thanks for the candle.

[*Noise of coal tub*]

Narrator: And the miner disappears into the darkness. George brings the stub of candle near to his crow, and the light catches the dull wooden eye. He smiles to himself. That's the second bit of candle he's had in two days. At the next gate is Jenny Burkinshaw. She's George's sister. Age 11 years. She talks to the darkness too. And the men when they go past.

Jenny: I love mam, I love pa. Talking to myself as if I'm mad. I love Peter, I love Paul. Oh those boys, I love 'em all. One two three four five six seven, when I'm dead I'll go to heaven. I think. I hope. [*Noise of tub in distance*] Here comes the tub. Rub-a-dub-dub. Here comes the coal. Through the hole.

[*Enter second Miner with coal tub*]

2nd Miner: Trap!!

Jenny: [*Calls out*] Hello.

2nd Miner: What is it, son?

Jenny: It's not son. It's me. Jenny Burkinshaw.

2nd Miner: Oh yes. Miss la di da Burkinshaw, is it?

Shut yer trap and yer trap. Get it. Shut yer trap and yer trap. Good 'un that. [*He goes. Noise of tub gets fainter until his second shout 'Trap!'*]

Jenny: [*To herself*] What a way to talk. Yer sit doing the gate for them and that's what you get. 'Shut yer trap and shut yer trap.' Eight nine ten eleven twelve. When I grow up I'll. . . . What rhymes with twelve?

2nd Miner: Trap!!

Narrator: Next in the line is William Price. Will the Whistler. And the next is Ann Moss. And sure enough, as he promised, William Price, trapper, age 13, who likes it in the mine, whistles his tune. [*He whistles*] And it reaches Ann Moss sitting on her stool by her gate down the long shaft.

Ann: [*To herself*] Thanks, Will. Don't stop. I hate the dark.

[*Change of lighting at this point is effective*]

Narrator: Summer comes. July 1838. July 4th. A warm day. Signs of a storm coming. Not a breath of wind. The fields bake in the hot sun. Corn begins to yellow. Black clouds begin to gather over Crane Moor. It's nearly two o'clock. Suddenly the heavens open and down it comes. Hailstones as big as baby's thumbs. [*Enter James Walker*] James Walker, coming from Barnsley Market, reaches the top of Keresforth Hill and looks down into Stainboro' Park. It's white over with the hail stones.

James Walker: My God. That's a right do, no mistake. Never seen owt like it. Them trappers will need sledges to get home. [*He crosses and exits*]

Narrator: But the trappers won't ever get home. [*Song – 'Wallflowers'. Lights dim again*] The hail turns to rain and it pours for two hours. Straight slanting rain, steaming up the hot land and soaking the green leaves. And finding its way underground by way of every hole, drain, cavern and opening in the earth. Underground and into the mine. A flash flood. Underground in Huskar pit, the children sit on their stools. Uriah Jubb, age 10, with his sister, Mary, at the next gate.

Uriah: There's water. I can hear water. [*Getting up and calling*] Mary! Mary! Are you there? Can you hear me? Mary! Come here to me.

Mary: [*Running towards him*] Uriah! That noise! What's up? I've left my gate, too. I'll be in trouble now.

Uriah: Never mind that. You've done right. Come with me. I know a place. Come on!

Mary: But my gate!

Uriah: Come on! [*They run off, or climb up to a higher level if possible*]

Narrator: And two children stumble and run into a little slit in the shaft. Uriah has heard about these things before. Floods in the mine. They are to be lucky. They crouch in the slit and watch the water rushing by – down to the other gates, the other children, sitting at their traps, waiting. Like Sarah Gooder, age 10. She's just going to eat her snap.

Sarah: [*Singing*] 'Do you know the muffin man, muffin man, muffin man?' [*To herself*] Shall I eat it now or keep it? Eat it now or keep it? Eat or keep? Eat! Got yer! [*Imitating her parents*] 'Don't talk with your mouth full, Sarah.' 'Why not?' 'We can't hear what you're saying.' What's that noise? I've never heard that before. I can see a star. I'm sure I can see a star. Lots of 'em. That's funny, that noise –

Narrator: And then the flood came. It crashed swirling through the workings, through all the traps one by one, and took the trappers with it. Little bodies picked off their stools and washed away in the dark like bits of twig.
Elizabeth Moss, age 14
Ann Moss, age 10
George Burkinshaw, age 12
Kathleen Palmer, age 9
Jenny Burkinshaw, age 11
Sarah Gooder, age 10
And many more, including William Price, age 13 'Whistling Willy Price'.

[*As the above narration is read out, children get up from their places one by one and go out. The sound of whistling comes over the loudspeaker*] The flood takes them all up and drowns them every one. Twenty-six children die that afternoon. Twenty-six young trappers between 7 and 17 years of age. The bodies come to rest against the bottom gate. The hailstones melt away in Stainboro' Park. The miners bring the bodies out. [*Enter* **Teasdale**] One of them, Robert Teasdale, would never forget.

Teasdale: I took the children to the farm near by. I washed the little white bodies and laid them out in the cart. One of them was gripping tight on a piece of wood shaped like a bird. I threw it away. Twenty-six bodies in all. Then I took them to their homes in the village where the mothers and fathers waited on their doorsteps to take back their children. There was weeping. And there was anger. They take the bodies in and close their doors. [*He stays, watching*]

Narrator: They are buried next day in one long grave. Side by side, the boys with the girls laid at their feet in another row. The village mourns. The Queen writes. She's not much older than some of them who died.

Queen Victoria: I must express my sorrow at your fearful loss.

Narrator: A mother stands at the long grave.

[*Enter* **mother**, *looking down at the grave*]

Mother: William. Give me back my William. God, give me back my whistling boy.

Narrator: But only the spade answers. And some crows circle overhead. Nasty, black things.

Song: Wallflowers, wallflowers.

The end

The Tree Machine

Mandy Alexander

Characters
Voices 1 to 6
Mr Rumbold   Chimney Sweep
Mrs Rumbold   his wife
Julie Rumbold   their daughter
Tom Dacre   new sweeping-boy
Darkie Dick   ⎫
Jack Higgins   ⎬   sweeping-boys
Joe Buggins   ⎭
Maid

The Tree Machine

Voice 1: When my mother died, I was very young,
And my father sold me while yet my tongue
Could scarcely cry 'Weep, weep, weep, weep!'
So your chimneys I sweep, and in soot I
sleep.

Voice 2: There's little Tom Dacre, who cried when
his head
That curled like a lamb's back was shaved.
So I said
'Hush, Tom! Never mind it – for when your
head's bare,
You know that the soot cannot spoil your
white hair.'

Voice 3: And so he was quiet. And that very night,
As Tom was a-sleeping, he had such a sight!
– That thousands of sweepers (Dick, Joe,
Ned and Jack)
Were all of them locked up in coffins of black.

Voice 4: And by came an Angel, who had a bright
key.
And he opened the coffins and set them all
free.

Then down a green plain, leaping, laughing,
  they run;
And wash in a river, and shine in the sun.

Voice 5: Then, naked and white, all their bags left
  behind,
They rise upon clouds, and sport in the wind.
And the Angel told Tom, if he'd be a good
  boy,
He'd have God for his father, and never
  want joy.

Voice 6: And so Tom awoke. And we rose in the dark,
And got with our bags and our brushes to
  work.
Though the morning was cold, Tom was
  happy and warm.
So if all do their duty, they need not fear
  harm.

1   Mr Rumbold's house. London, in the year 1803

Mrs Rumbold *and her daughter* **Julie** *are sitting
sewing.*

Julie: Ma, what time will our dad be in?

Mrs Rumbold: Any time now, dear. He's gone to pick
up the new boy.

Julie: The new boy from the orphanage?

Mrs Rumbold: Yes, love. Nice little boy, by all
accounts.

Julie: How do you mean, ma - 'nice'?

Mrs Rumbold: Well, thin. Real thin. But strong,

mind, and healthy looking. Just right for the trade.

Julie: Have you seen him, ma?

Mrs Rumbold: No, I ain't seen him, Julie, but your dad has. The Beadle came round yesterday and told him the good news.

Julie: I suppose it *was* good news, wasn't it, ma?

Mrs Rumbold: Yes. Good, thin, strong lads don't come to the orphanage every day of the week. Just what we wanted – a new boy. We've had far too many running away lately.

Julie: Will we ever get them back again, ma?

Mrs Rumbold: Maybe we will, and maybe we won't. Crafty little beggars, most of them. They get clean away. But then there's the other kind.

Julie: What kind's that, ma?

Mrs Rumbold: The kind as jumps in the river, Julie. No sense of gratitude. They ain't got no thought for Mr Rumbold, and him with all those chimneys to clean for the gentry. Little heathens they must be. I hope the new boy's a bit better. [*A door slams*] That'll be your dad now. We'll soon see what he's brought.

[*Enter* **Mr Rumbold**, *the Chimney Sweep, with young* **Tom Dacre**]

Mr Rumbold: Now then, Mrs R. See what I've gone and brought yer. [*Pulling* **Tom** *forward by his ear*] What do you think of that, then?

Mrs Rumbold: [*Examining* **Tom** *and feeling his*

muscles] Right little corker, Charlie, and no mistake. What do you say, Julie?

Julie: He'll do. Same as all boys, I reckon. [*She pinches him*] What's his name, dad?

Mr Rumbold: Go on, boy. Answer Miss Julie when she speaks to yer!

Tom: Please miss, it's Tom, miss.

Julie: Tom who?

Tom: Tom Dacre, miss.

Julie: Dacre, Dacre, thin as a raker! [*She sticks out her tongue*]

Mrs Rumbold: Now then, Julie. Mustn't make fun of the little lad. He's just right for the gentry's chimneys, he is. Reckon you've got a good 'un there, Charlie. Is he ready for Going Up?

Mr Rumbold: 'Course he is! First thing tomorrow morning. Five o'clock sharp.

Mrs Rumbold: Whose chimney will you be sweeping then?

Mr Rumbold: Let me see now. That'll be Mr Kingsley's chimney.

Mrs Rumbold: Oh, the Reverend Kingsley, do you mean?

Mr Rumbold: Yes, Mrs R. The new minister, as ever was. It'll be our chance to get to know him. Tom, me lad, you should be very proud to think that your very first chimney belongs to the Reverend Charles Kingsley.

Mrs Rumbold: A very clever man he is, they say. Writes books, even!

Mr Rumbold: See what a high-class trade you've got into, boy?

Julie: Isn't he thin? He'd make a good scarecrow!

2 The room where the sweeping-boys sleep.

It is very dark. Somebody is crying.

Darkie Dick: Sh! [*Then louder*] Sh! Sh! Which of you lads is making all that noise? Waking up a poor chimney-sweeping lad in the middle of the night! Why don't you get some kip? [*There is silence for a minute, then more sniffing*] Cut it out! Which one of you lads is it? Is it you, Joe? [*No reply*] Ned, is it you? [*No reply*] Jack Higgins – is it you snivelling, lad? [*No reply*] I know who it must be. It's that new little whelp. Is it the new boy that's a-snivelling?

Tom: Please, sir, yes sir.

Darkie: Here, who are you calling 'sir'? Are you trying to be funny?

Tom: Oh, no sir. I just feel miserable, sir.

Darkie: And what might you be miserable about?

Tom: Please, sir – I ain't never been up a chimney before, and I'm scared.

Darkie: Scared, are you? Well, you wouldn't be the first boy to tell me that he's scared. And what in particular might be scaring you?

Tom: Please, sir: what's it like?

Darkie: Sweeping a chimney? It's black, boy. Black!

Tom: Is it as black as it is now, sir?

Darkie: Here, stop calling me 'sir'. As a matter of fact, it's much blacker, and a whole lot smellier. That's what I don't like – the soot. [*He coughs*] Gets in your tubes, the soot does. You'll know all about that tomorrow, young fellow-me-lad. What's your name, then?

Tom: Please sir, it's Tom.

Darkie: For Gawd's sake don't call me 'sir'! I'll have to come over there and clip you one. I'm Dick. Darkie Dick. I ain't got no other real name.

Tom: Please, Darkie, will you tell me about –

Voice: Will you two shut up? I want to get some sleep!

Darkie: Is that you, Jack Higgins?

Jack: Yes, Darkie Dick. And just you watch out tomorrow. Waking us all up in the middle of the night!

Darkie: It's this new boy, Jack. Name of Tom. It was him as woke me up in the first place. Little lad's Going Up for the first time tomorrow, and he can't sleep.

Jack: First time, eh? Cor! I remember my first chimney. No wonder he can't sleep. And he won't sleep tomorrow night either, for thinking about it.

2nd Voice: What's the matter with you lot? What's going on, eh?

Jack: That you, Joe? Wake up and join the party.

Joe: Party, what party?

Jack: We've got a new boy here, Joe. Tom's his name. He's Going Up tomorrow.

Joe: For the first time?

Jack: Yes – for the first time. Wants to know what it's like! [**Joe** *laughs half-wittedly*] What are you laughing at, Joe?

Joe: Hope he gets stuck!

Jack: You're a right monster you are, Joe. You like it when the new lads get stuck, don't you? Peculiar sense of humour, has Joe.

Tom: What does he mean, Darkie, when he says 'stuck'?

Darkie: Jammed. Like a cork in a bleeding bottle.

Jack: It ain't no fun being jammed. I've been jammed.

Joe: Who ain't been jammed? I've been jammed too. So's everybody, one time or another.

Darkie: Cor, makes you feel like you were dying, Tom. Makes you wish you *was* dying. You don't never want to get stuck, Tom, not if you can help it.

Jack: If you do, though – don't struggle.

Joe: Struggling brings the soot down.

Jack: Makes you jam tighter. Soot in your eyes, soot in your mouth, soot in your ears. It's horrible!

Joe: Rumbold knows how to get you out, though, don't he? He's a great one for getting you un-stuck, is Rumbold.

[*They all laugh, and then are suddenly silent*]

Tom: Well, what does he do?

Darkie: He has his ways, Tom, he has his ways. . . .

Joe: He lights a fire, that's what he does. Down in the grate.

Jack: You don't stay stuck for long with Mr Rumbold!

Joe: Toasts your toes, he does!

Darkie: Oh, yes, Tom. You don't stay stuck for long with Mr Rumbold!

3   Outside the Rev. Charles Kingsley's house

Mr Rumbold *holding* **Tom** *by the scruff of the neck, knocks on the door. It is opened by a maidservant.*

Mr Rumbold: Morning, miss. Rumbold's the name. Come to sweep the chimney. Mr Kingsley in?

Maid: What's that you've got with you? A bit of bent wire?

Mr Rumbold: My new lad, miss. Say hello, Tom.

Tom: 'Morning, miss.

Maid: Well, come inside both of you and mind you don't make no mess. And don't make no noise, either. Mr Kingsley's got a guest. An inventor!

Mr Rumbold: Now then, Tom – did you hear that? An inventor! I told you that when you worked for Charlie Rumbold you worked for class! And what sort of inventions does the gentlemen invent, might I ask?

Maid: How should I know? Umbrellas, I should think, judging by the queer things he's brought with him.

But never you mind. That's Mr Kingsley's business, that is, not yours. And mind you make a good job of his study chimney. Been smoking something horrible it has, all winter.

Mr Rumbold: Should have called me sooner, miss. Should never leave a chimney till the last minute.

Maid: It's not my fault, to be sure. I'd have called you months ago. It's Mr Kingsley. He has some funny ideas about chimney-sweeping.

Mr Rumbold: How do you mean, miss – 'funny ideas'?

Maid: Well, I don't think he likes having them done somehow. Says he doesn't like to see the little lads climbing up. Yes, he's got some very funny ideas has Mr Kingsley. But he's a nice man really, when you get to know him. A very kind-hearted man. Writes books, you know. So mind you don't get no soot on any of his papers, or there'll be trouble. Follow me, and I'll take you to his study.

4   Back at Mr Rumbold's house, later in the day

The door opens, and in comes a furious **Rumbold** *followed by a terrified* **Tom.**

Mr Rumbold: Mad, he is. Stark, staring, raving *mad*!

Mrs Rumbold: [*Coming in from the kitchen*] Is that you, Mr R?

Mr Rumbold: Yes, it is me. Or else I'm out of my mind!

Mrs Rumbold: Out of your mind? What do you mean?

Mr Rumbold: I think I must be losing my marbles, wife. Else, why would I be here in the middle of the morning, with a living to earn? Sit down, and I'll tell you all about it. [*They gather round the table*] It was like this, see? I was just about to shove young Tom here up the chimney - on his first climb, like - wasn't I?

Tom: Yes, sir.

Mr Rumbold: And we was in Mr Kingsley's study, wasn't we?

Tom: Yes, Mr Rumbold, sir.

Mr Rumbold: When all of a sudden - all of a sudden - all of *a sudden!* - in comes Mr Kingsley with a *man!* Cor!

Mrs Rumbold: Husband, pull yourself together! Whatever is the matter with you? What's wrong with seeing Mr Kingsley?

Mr Rumbold: But - he came in with a man!

Mrs Rumbold: You've seen a man before, husband!

Mr Rumbold: But this man had - a *machine!*

Mrs Rumbold: A machine? What kind of a machine?

Tom: Please, mum - it was all queer! It was like a tree!

Mr Rumbold: Like a tree it was, wife, as sure as I'm sitting here.

Mrs Rumbold: A machine like a tree! Whatever was it for?

Mr Rumbold: [*Groaning*] I daren't tell you, wife. It's too horrible to think about. Too horrible. Can you guess what that machine was for?

Mrs Rumbold: Go on – tell me.

Mr Rumbold: That there machine was nothing more nor nothing less than a *chimney-sweeping machine.*

Mrs Rumbold: A *what*?

Mr Rumbold: A chimney-sweeping machine! I think the end of the world has come!

Mrs Rumbold: A chimney-sweeping machine? What in the name of goodness can that be?

Mr Rumbold: I ain't got the words to describe it. You tell her, Tom lad.

Tom: Well, it was sort of sticks, Mrs Rumbold. Lots of sticks. And one of the sticks had a sort of brush at the end.

Mr Rumbold: Like a tree, Mrs R, like a tree.

Mrs Rumbold: Like a tree? I'm sure my poor head's in a dreadful muddle!

Mr Rumbold: I'll show you what I mean. Tom, stand on that table! [**Tom** *does as he is told*] Now Tom's like a stick, ain't he? Now suppose his arms were brushes! Hanging down at his sides, all limp-like. And suppose I had in mind to pull one of his legs? Just see what happens. [*He pulls at one of* **Tom***'s legs.* **Tom***'s arms shoot out*]

Mrs Rumbold: I still don't see what you mean.

Mr Rumbold: Well, it's like this. The machine is made of sticks, all joined together. They sort of twist

and click. The end one is made like young Tom here.
Narrow, very narrow, to begin with. Very easy to slide
up the chimney, pushing up from the bottom, a bit at
a time. Then *whoosh!*

Mrs Rumbold: Whoosh? How do you mean,
'whoosh'?

Mr Rumbold: All of a sudden, you pull a bit of rope
that's threaded inside the sticks, and whoosh! the
arms stick out, the full width of the chimney. And in
the case of the chimney-sweeping machine, them
arms is *brushes!* [**Mr Rumbold** *demonstrates, using*
Tom. *He pulls a leg, and* **Tom**'s *arms shoot out*] And
what's more, them brushes can be *twirled!* [**Mr
Rumbold** *twirls* **Tom** *round*] And they can be *moved
up and down!* [**Tom** *demonstrates by bending up and
down at the knees*] See what I mean?

Mrs Rumbold: It's diabolical, that's what it is.
Diabolical. And what did Mr Kingsley have to say
about all this?

Mr Rumbold: Well, Mrs R, he saw me getting ready to
shove young Tom here up the chimney, and he said
'Mr Rumbold' – he said – 'Put that boy down!'

Mrs Rumbold: Put him down – when you was getting
ready to put him up?

Mr Rumbold: 'Put that boy down,' he said. To me,
Charlie Rumbold, Master Chimney Sweeper, what's
never had a bad word said about him by anybody in
all his twenty-five years in the trade. 'Put that boy
down,' he said, 'and don't come back here no more
until you've got yourself a machine!' And before you
could say 'Lord Shaftesbury', he'd shown us the door,
like we was common tramps.

Tom: He gave me this, mum. [*Showing* **Mrs Rumbold** *a piece of paper*]

Mr Rumbold: It's got writing on it, Mrs R, and drawings of that there machine. Read out what it says, Mrs R – you've got more book learning than me.

Mrs Rumbold: [*Taking it over to the light*] It says here: 'Those who have long viewed the wretchedness to which many children are exposed, in climbing chimneys – '

Mr Rumbold: Wretchedness? Climbing chimneys?

Mrs Rumbold: '– and who think it a disgrace to our age –'

Mr Rumbold: Disgrace? Climbing chimneys ain't no disgrace!

Mrs Rumbold: – 'will congratulate Mr Smart on his timely invention.'

Mr Rumbold: Congratulate him? Suffocate him more likely!

Mrs Rumbold: '– for it has proved that climbing boys are no longer required in the proper cleaning of a chimney.' Oh, Mr Rumbold, did you ever hear such a monstrous piece of libel and slander?

Mr Rumbold: What's the world coming to? I ask you: is there no sense of justice? It's the end of the world, wife, when chimney sweepers can't earn an honest living.

Mrs Rumbold: That Reverend Kingsley! And he calls himself a Christian!

Mr Rumbold: Tom, lad. This is just the beginning.

Machines is taking away the livings of honest orphans. Today it's chimneys. Tomorrow it'll be jobs of all descriptions.

Mrs Rumbold: They'll be sending you to school next!

Mr Rumbold: Them and their Tree Machines!

The end

The Awful Billy Smiff

Brian Jacques

Characters
Miss Carmody Deputy Head
Miss Crampton new teacher
Mr Howard geography teacher
Mr Cunningham history teacher
Rachel
Billy Smiff
Jennifer
Susan
Miriam   } Form 2C
George
Peter
Ian

The Awful Billy Smiff

---

1 A school staffroom

It is the beginning of term. The three teachers present look very depressed. There is a knock at the door.

Mrs Carmody: Come in!

[*A young woman teacher,* **Miss Crampton,** *walks in, all smiles*]

Miss Crampton: Good morning. I'm Liz Crampton, the new teacher.

Mrs Carmody: Oh, good. Do come in, Miss Crampton. I'm Mrs Carmody, the Deputy Head, and these two gentlemen here are Mr Howard, our geography master, and Mr Cunningham who teaches history.

Mr Howard:
Mr Cunningham: } Hello.

Miss Crampton: Pleased to meet you.

Mrs Carmody: Do sit down. Like a cup of tea?

Miss Crampton: That would be nice. Yes, please.
[**Miss Crampton** *sits down and* **Mrs Carmody** *gives her a cup of tea. They all sit in complete silence*

looking very unhappy. **Miss Crampton** *then says cheerfully*] Well, I know this is the first day of the new term, and I hope I'm not being too rude, but why all the long faces?

Mr Cunningham: The sword of Damocles my dear, the sword of Damocles.

Miss Crampton: [*Puzzled*] I'm afraid I'm not quite with you.

Mr Howard: Let me explain. The reason we're looking so worried is that we haven't been told yet which classes we'll be taking this term.

Miss Crampton: But surely one class is much the same as another?

Mrs Carmody: [*Drily*] I take it that this is your first teaching appointment?

Miss Crampton: Well yes. But what's that to do with it?

Mrs Carmody: [*Turning to* **Mr Cunningham** *and* **Mr Howard**] Poor girl! Obviously she's never heard of 2C.

Mr Howard: [*Covering his ears*] Do you mind not mentioning that dreadful class? I'm only a poor weak Geography teacher.

Miss Crampton: What's so wrong with 2C, then?

Mr Cunningham: If I have to take 2C this year, I'll tie two medicine balls around my neck and jump into the school swimming pool, I really will!

Miss Crampton: But I've just come from the Headmaster's study, and he told me that *I'll* be taking 2C this term.

[*The three teachers give a huge sigh of relief and slump back into their chairs, smiling blissfully*]

Mr Howard: Oh, happy day!

Mr Cunningham: I feel like going out and getting stoned!

Mrs Carmody: If I were not the Deputy Head, I'd join you.

Miss Crampton: Excuse me, but I'm still in the dark about all this. Is there something wrong with 2C?

Mrs Carmody: [*All innocence*] Wrong? Why should there be anything wrong?

Mr Cunningham: You'll have a perfectly delightful classroom. All modern equipment, French windows, lots of fresh air, central heating.

Mr Howard: And the children! The children are delightful little ten-year-olds. Clean, polite, intelligent – you'll love them, Miss Crampton.

Miss Crampton: Good, then I've nothing to worry about.

Mrs Carmody: [*Turning serious*] Shall we tell her?

Miss Crampton: Tell me what?

Mr Cunningham: No, she looks so happy. Why spoil her day?

Miss Crampton: Please tell me. Is there, perhaps, a problem child?

[*The other three teachers laugh*]

Mrs Carmody: Child, she called him a child!

Mr Howard: A bit like calling a tiger a pussycat, I suppose.

Mr Cunningham: Or a werewolf a doggie.

[*The three teachers start laughing again*]

Miss Crampton: I do wish you'd stop all this joking and tell me who you're talking about.

Mrs Carmody: His name is Billy Smiff!

Miss Crampton: Billy Smiff?

Mrs Carmody:
Mr Howard: } Billy Smiff!!!
Mr Cunningham:

Miss Crampton: Well, let me reassure you. I did a course on problem children at college, and I've still got my lecture notes and essays.

Mr Cunningham: Marvellous. But Billy Smiff is a special case.

Miss Crampton: Oh, come now. He can't be all that bad.

Mr Howard: I was Billy Smiff's geography master last term. Let me read you some of the answers he gave in the exams. [*He produces a large grubby paper*] Question one: Where is Sydney? Answer, 'He is sitting behind Margaret.' Question two: What do you know about Peking? Answer, 'Dear Sir, I am taking a mark off you for your spelling. Peeking is what nosy people do through keyholes.' Do you want me to go any further, Miss Crampton?

Miss Crampton: If you wish.

Mr Howard: Question three: Where do Poles live? Answer: 'At the North and South Poles.' I could go on and on. Billy Smiff knows as much about Geography as my budgerigar knows about brain surgery.

Miss Crampton: But surely he did better in his other subjects?

Mr Cunningham: Do you think so? Just let me read you a bit of Billy Smiff's history exam paper.

Miss Crampton: Was it outstanding?

Mr Cunningham: It was. He was the only boy in the entire school to receive a mark of minus twenty.

Miss Crampton: Impossible!

Mr Cunningham: My dear young lady, I can assure you. With Billy Smiff, anything is possible. [*He produces another large grubby paper*] Question three: Who won the War of the Roses? Answer: 'Cadbury's'. Question six was a classic. Listen to this. What is another name for a Norseman? Answer: 'A cowboy'.

Miss Crampton: Good Lord, is he really that awful?

Mr Cunningham: Those were a few of his better ones. The final question on the History paper was: Where did King Charles hide from Cromwell's men? Do you know what Billy Smiff answered?

Miss Crampton: I shudder to think.

Mr Cunningham: And well you may. Here's his answer. 'King Charles hid from the Roundheads in the Royal Oak.' Then he crossed that out and put 'Red Lion'. Then he crossed that out and put 'The Station Arms'. Then he crossed the lot out and wrote 'King Charles hid from Cromwell's men in one of those pubs

on the High Street, but I've forgotten which one.' How
about that?

Miss Crampton: I can't believe it. Was he serious, or
was he having you on?

Mrs Carmody: We don't really know. I had Billy
Smiff in my class two terms ago, before I had my
nervous breakdown.

Miss Crampton: Nervous breakdown? Whatever
brought that on?

Mrs Carmody:
Mr Howard: } Billy Smiff!

Miss Crampton: [*Beginning to realize*] Oh dear. I've
got a problem on my hands, haven't I?

Mrs Carmody: Indeed, you have. Any boy who
thinks bad grammar is a wicked Nanna is bound to
be a problem.

Mr Howard: He's rather good at sport, though.

Mr Cunningham: You must be joking, Mr Howard.
What makes you say that?

Mr Howard: Well, he taught all the girls in my class
to box, and for Sports Day he introduced a whole new
range of events that he invented himself. Of course,
he won them all. The egg in the sack race; the one
metre sprint; the one-man relay race. The Headmaster still hasn't bought me a new track suit, after
what Billy Smiff did to my old one with his javelin. . . .

Miss Crampton: [*Suddenly determined*] Right, then
I will be very firm with this Billy Smiff. That's the
answer.

Mr Cunningham: His mother and father tried being

firm with him. I wouldn't advise you to try it.

Miss Crampton: Why ever not?

Mr Cunningham: You might end up like them.

Miss Crampton: What sort of people are they, his parents?

Mrs Carmody: Frail, wrinkled, nervous little old people with grey hair. His mother is twenty-seven and his father is twenty-eight.

Miss Crampton: Oh, no. . . .

[*The bell rings loudly for first lesson, concealing her cry of anguish*]

2 2C's classroom

The door opens and **Miss Crampton** *walks boldly in, as befits one who has attended lectures on discipline, and written essays on the subject.*

Miss Crampton: [*In a firm voice*] Good morning, children. I'm your new teacher. My name is Miss Crampton. [*She writes it clearly on the blackboard as per the rule book*]

All Children: [*Sweetly*] Good morning, Miss Crampton.

Rachel: Please miss, Billy Smiff has taken my netball badge.

Miss Crampton: [*Straight into no-nonsense action*] Has he? Right! Where is Billy Smiff?

[**Billy Smiff**, *all four foot nothing of him, rises to his feet with the elegance of a lame camel*]

Billy: Here miss. I never took Rachel's netball badge. Silly little round badge with a pin! What would I want with that? She'll probably find it in a minute, stuck in her –

Miss Crampton: [*Interrupting; this is no time for taking chances*] Silence! When I wish you to speak, Billy Smiff, I'll ask you to do so. Now Rachel, did you actually see Billy take your netball badge?

Rachel: No miss, but I could tell he had it by the way he was laughing.

Miss Crampton: Rachel, you should never accuse anyone of stealing if you have no proof. As Billy said, you will probably find it quite soon. So sit down.

Rachel: [*Sits down and jumps up with a scream*] Oooooh, it was on the seat!

Billy: See, I told you you'd soon find it!

Miss Crampton: Billy Smiff, if I thought for one moment that you had put that badge on Rachel's seat, with the pin sticking up, I would deal with you most severely.

Billy: Who, me? I never did it Miss. I get the blame for everything in this class! Just because I'm Billy Smiff.

Miss Crampton: You can rest assured I won't blame you for anything, Billy Smiff, unless I have definite proof. So sit down, and we'll say no more about it.

Billy: [*To the class, but still on his feet*] Did you all hear that? A good fair teacher. That's what I like.

Someone who doesn't keep blaming me for everything. It's about time the Headmaster gave me a good teacher. I've suffered long enough.

Miss Crampton: [*Determined to be boss*] Billy Smiff, *sit down*! Now everybody, take out your general subjects exercise book and turn to a clean page.

Billy: [*Seated now, and searching frantically through his rubbish-tip of a desk*] Miss, miss, this page is clean except for where my frog jumped on it last term and got squashed. Will that do, miss?

Miss Crampton: Yes. But one more word from you, Billy Smiff, and I shall get really cross with you. Do you understand?

[**Billy** *says nothing*]

Miss Crampton: [*Not missing a trick*] Billy Smiff, I said 'Do you understand?'

Billy: 'Course I do, miss. But you said one more word from me and you'd be really cross, so I shut up, miss.

Rachel: [*Who has been through scenes like this before*] Take no notice of him, miss.

Miss Crampton: [*Not yet in need of moral support*] Thank you Rachel, but when I want your opinion I shall ask for it. Right, now who knows what day it is today?

Billy: Pancake Tuesday, Miss.

Miss Crampton: You silly boy, it is Monday the sixth of September.

Billy: Well, if you knew that Miss, why were you asking us?

Miss Crampton: I was just testing you.

Billy: Oh, I see. We don't usually have tests till the end of term. Seeing as you are new here, Miss, we'll let you off.

[*The children start laughing.* **Miss Crampton** *thinks of her lectures and essays back at college, and bawls*]

Miss Crampton: Silence! Stop this silly laughing at once! At once, I say! [*The voice of authority wins – the children stop laughing, and the lesson begins*] Are you paying attention? [*Everyone, including* **Billy***, looks suitably angelic*] Right. Today we will deal with proverbs, morals and sayings.

Billy: [*Hand up in a flash*] Please miss, I know all about proverbs and morals and sayings.

Miss Crampton: Billy Smiff, will you please be quiet and let me explain the point of the lesson to the rest of the class.

Jennifer: Please miss, Billy Smiff thinks he knows everything.

Miss Crampton: Yes, I've no doubt he does. But there's an old proverb that says, 'A little knowledge is a dangerous thing'.

Billy: Miss, my ma says that I'm a dangerous thing.

Miss Crampton: [*Quick to score*] Your mother is absolutely right. [*The class titters obligingly*] But note the word is 'mother', not 'ma'. 'My *mother* says that I am a dangerous thing.'

Billy: [*Delighted*] Does she, miss? Then you must be the same as me.

Jennifer: Oh, do shut up Billy. Let Miss Crampton get on with the lesson.

Billy: They shouldn't allow dangerous teachers in schools.

Miss Crampton: [*Getting rather strained*] But I'm not a dangerous teacher, Billy Smiff.

Billy: [*Light dawns*] Oh, I see miss. You're only dangerous when you're at home with your ma.

Miss Crampton: [*Deciding on quick retreat*] Please, Billy, be quiet and let me get on with the lesson. First let me tell you a little story. The other day, when I arrived home from school, there was no one at home. I had forgotten to take my key with me that morning. . . .

Billy: [*Irrepressible*] So you had to climb through the bedroom window, miss!

Miss Crampton: [*Action at last; no messing*] Go and stand in the corner, Billy Smiff, this minute! [**Billy** *lumbers to his feet and stands in the corner with his back to* **Miss Crampton**] Now, as I was saying. There was no one at home and I had forgotten my key. 'What shall I do?' I wondered. It was just at that moment that my mother arrived back from shopping. Luckily she had her own key with her, so she opened the door, and we both went inside, and had a strawberry tea. I said to myself 'All's well that ends well'.

Jennifer: Oh, that was nice, miss.

Miss Crampton: Thank you, Jennifer.

Billy: It would have been nicer if you'd climbed in through the bedroom window, miss –

Miss Crampton: [*Action again*] Take one hundred lines, Billy Smiff.

Billy: [*In full flow*] – just like a burglar, and you could have worn a black mask!

Miss Crampton: [*Determined to win*] Take *two* hundred lines Billy Smiff! And if you speak again, I'll give you three hundred lines. Understand? [**Billy** *seems to get the message*] Now, that little story was an example of a tale with a moral, proverb or saying, at the end of it. Is there any boy or girl in the class who would like to tell me a story that ends with a moral? [*Some of the boys and girls raise their hands*]

Billy: [*Raises his hand and waves it about shouting*] Miss, miss, I know one miss! I know a great story, miss!

Miss Crampton: [*Ignores* **Billy***, and selects a girl*] Susan, would you like to tell us your story?

Susan: Please miss, last Saturday I was at the super-market and I saw a lady drop her purse. She didn't know she had dropped it, so I picked the purse up and gave it back to her. She was very happy, and gave me fifty pence as a reward, miss.

Miss Crampton: How nice. Tell me, Susan, what was the moral of that little story?

Susan: Honesty is the best policy, miss.

Miss Crampton: Very good Susan, very good indeed. Has anyone else got a story to tell?

[*All raise their hands again*]

Billy: [*Raises both hands and starts to shout*] Miss,

miss, let me tell one miss! I know a good one, miss! You'll like this one, miss! It's very exciting, miss!

[**Miss Crampton** *pretends she has not noticed* **Billy Smiff**]

Miss Crampton: Miriam. Tell us your story.

Miriam: The other day I was playing with my friends. I fell over and tore my jeans. I ran straight home to my mother, and she sewed them for me. Mother said it was only a tiny tear, and very easy to mend, 'cos it only needed one stitch.

Miss Crampton: [*Smiling*] Thanks, Miriam. I think we can all guess the moral of Miriam's tale. George, do you know what it is?

George: Yes, miss, 'A stitch in time saves nine.'

Miss Crampton: Excellent. We've time for one or two more . . . anybody?

Billy: [*Jumping about wildly waving his arms and his legs*] Oh, come on, miss! Ask me please! I've got a smashing one.

Miss Crampton: [*Still deliberately blind*] Yes Peter, I see your hand is up.

Peter: Miss, there's a big fierce dog that lives in my road. He barks at people and bites them if he gets a chance. But he is very friendly to me, because I used to feed him and stroke him when he was a puppy.

Miss Crampton: That was very good of you Peter. I wonder what the moral to Peter's story can possibly be. Would you like to tell us?

Peter: My father says the moral is, 'A little kindness goes a long way'.

Miss Crampton: And how right your father is, Peter. Good, just time for one last story now.

Billy: [*Runs up and climbs on top of the desk in front of* **Miss Crampton**. *He jumps about, waving his arms madly*] Miss, if you don't let me tell my story, I'll jump off this desk and break both my legs. It's the best story in the world, miss. Please, miss, let me have a go miss . . . miss . . . miss . . . miss. [*He is shouting very loud.* **Miss Crampton** *covers her ears*]

Miss Crampton: Billy Smiff, will you please stop shouting. You are giving me a headache.

Billy: Well, let me tell my story then! Go on miss, please, and I promise I'll be good for the rest of my life! Honest, cross my heart and hope to die, miss. [*He climbs down from the desk and crosses his heart*]

Miss Crampton: [*Yielding to the inevitable*] Oh, very well. But keep your voice down and make the story brief.

Billy: [*Paces up and down the room with both hands clasped behind his back. He stops in front of* **Miss Crampton** *and looks her squarely in the eye then begins. As he speaks he waves his arms about and performs all the story as he is telling it*] Well, miss, all this happened about a week ago, last Tuesday I think it was . . . no, wait a minute, I tell a lie, it was Saturday afternoon after the matinée let out at the pictures –

Ian: No, it was Thursday lunchtime. You were playing football with me on Saturday, Billy.

Billy: I was not! Anyhow, who asked you to butt in,

Ian Jones? I'll give you a belt on the nose if you don't shut up.

Miss Crampton: [*Still in charge*] Billy Smiff! How dare you! Be quiet! I mean, get on with it!

Billy: Get on with what, miss?

Miss Crampton: The story.

Billy: Oh, that? Right, well where was I? Oh, yes. I was coming out of the pictures last Saturday, when I suddenly noticed two big lads following me. They looked very big and tough, just like two muggers.

Miss Crampton: How awful. What did you do, Billy?

Billy: Look, who's telling this story, miss, me or you?

Miss Crampton: [*Resigned*] You are, Billy.

Billy: Good. Then would you kindly belt up, er, I mean be quiet and let me get on with it? Now, as I said, there was these two great big muggers following me.

Jennifer: Why were they following you?

Billy: How should I know? Shut up, Jenny Greenwood. Well, I started walking pretty fast, but I was whistling too, like this [*He does a small whistle*] but they were getting closer and closer.

Miss Crampton: Good heavens. What was the moral?

Billy: [*Ignoring her*] Anyway, as soon as I got round the corner by the gate I started to run. I'm a great runner as you all know, but as I looked behind me, guess what?

Miss Crampton: Oh dear, what?

Billy: [*Still ignoring her*] I looked around and I saw these two great big huge muggers running after me. They were shouting 'Come here Billy Smiff, we are going to beat you up.' But I just ran as fast as my legs could carry me, right down the road and around the corner by the church. I must have been doing fifty miles an hour but they were close behind me, running so fast that smoke was coming from their boots.

Miss Crampton: [*Holding up her hands in horror*] Oh, the dreadful bullies. What was the moral?

Billy: [*Still ignoring her*] So I ducked down the alley by the side of the shops. My laces were both undone but I still kept going. I could feel their hot breath on the back of my neck. They were getting closer.

George: And did they catch you, Billy, did they, did they?

Billy: [*Too involved to answer*] Straight out the alley I shot, and up the avenue towards the park, dodging in and out of all the gardens. But they were sticking close on my heels. I was panting for breath: pant, pant. And gasping too: gasp, gasp. I must have been going about sixty-five miles an hour by this time, but these two huge gigantic bullies were right behind me.

Miss Crampton: Oh, I feel faint.

Billy: So did I miss, but I kept running.

Miss Crampton: Oh Billy, what was the moral? Did they catch you?

Billy: No. They couldn't catch me miss, because they were only doing sixty-four miles an hour. Oh boy, were my legs getting tired! But I didn't care. Straight into the park I went. Right behind me they were, so I climbed up the slide and slid down, went three times round the swings, jumped over the railings and hurtled through the bushes out into the crescent.

Miss Crampton: Oh dear. What was the moral?

Billy: Do y'know, I thundered along that crescent and right behind me those two ten-foot high muggers were still coming after me, shouting 'Billy Smiff is going to get thumped!'

Miss Crampton: But what was the moral? Please tell us!

Billy: I skidded around the corner of the crescent on one foot. The sweat was pouring off me. Right down the High Street I ran. People were jumping out of the way as the three of us tore past. I turned quickly and dashed down a little alley between two shops, and there at the bottom was a great big brick wall. I could go no further miss, I was trapped.

Miss Crampton: Oh, no. What was the moral?

Billy: [*Still ignoring* **Miss Crampton**] There I was, the great Billy Smiff, caught like a rat in a trap. [*Throws his arms wide and looks about desperately*] Suddenly, one of these twelve-foot high muggers pulls out a big piece of wood and tries to hit me.

Miss Crampton: Oh, you poor boy!

Billy: [*Carrying straight on*] Ha ha, but I did a bit of Kung Fu and suddenly grabbed the wood off him. Smack! I hit him on the head. I had to jump up high because he was fifteen feet tall. Down he went like a log, miss.

Miss Crampton: Oh, you brave boy! Now, what was the moral?

Billy: [*Still ignoring* **Miss Crampton**] Then the other hooligan put up his fists and tried to hit me. But I dodged round him and thwack! I smacked him on the nut with the wood and he went down like a ton of bricks, because he was sixteen feet tall, miss.

Miss Crampton: [*Getting to the end of her tether*] Oh, I can't bear it. What was the moral?

Billy: [*Still in full flight*] So then the two of them were on the floor. They were shouting, 'O mercy, Billy Smiff. Please let us go.' But I didn't let them go. Oh, no! I jumped on them, and I gave them a left and I gave them a right, and I smacked them in the face, and I kicked them in the bottom, and I hit them with the wood, and I jumped on them, and I did a bit more Kung Fu, and I bounced all over them, and I hit. . . .

Miss Crampton: [*Suddenly cuts in and roars at the top of her voice. Her tether is fractions of an inch away*] Billy Smiff! I can't take any more! What . . . was . . . the . . . moral . . . ?

Billy: Well, miss, the moral is. . . . [*The whole room is in suspense. The pause is cleverly calculated. Just as the strain is beyond endurance,* **Billy** *speaks again*] The moral is . . . You don't mess with Billy Smiff!!!

[*There is an awful silence.* **Miss Crampton** *slowly collapses in a quivering heap. She begins to sob quietly as the bell rings for the end of the lesson. The class pauses a moment, then claps appreciatively.* **Billy** *clasps his hands together over his head* *in acknowledgement. The door opens and* **Mrs Carmody** *looks in*]

Mrs Carmody: Billy Smiff – you've done it again!

The end

Darren's Conker

Anne Pickles

Characters

The Leader } creatures from another planet
Spaceman

Miss Brown   a teacher

Darren Wildgoose
Mark Tyler
Joanne Wilson
Tracey Blagden
Linda Cawthorne
Stephen Marshall   } the class
Glenroy Williams
Cheryl Bates
John Cavendish
Michelle Benson
Denise Jones

Mr Stuart   Headmaster
Mr Driscoll   Caretaker

Teachers are welcome to perform this play and to alter and adapt it to suit their needs. The author would, however, be glad to hear of any public performance, and to offer advice and assistance if required. Please contact her c/o BBC Radio Sheffield.

Darren's Conker

1   A spaceship

*Creatures from another planet are approaching Earth.
The **Leader**, who is very small, speaks scribble all the
time. The **Spaceman** translates.*

Leader: Nick wok yen ton vickle (etc, etc.)

Spaceman: [*Speaks all on one note like a Dalek*] We
are searching. We are searching. We are searching.
We are searching for a suitable Earth-spot to rest. We
are coming to Earth for peaceful purposes. We wish to
find a group of top-rank Earthlings. We have been
preparing for this mission for twenty-five earth years.
Take us to your leaders. Take us to your leaders. Take
us to your leaders.

[*The spaceship hums loudly; then, as it lands, there
is a silence*]

2   A school classroom

It is a maths lesson.

Miss Brown: Darren Wildgoose, stop fidgeting and
concentrate.

Darren: [*Sitting at the back*] Yes, Miss Brown.

Miss Brown: Now, who's going to help me to do this sum on the board? Hands up, please.

Mark: Me, me, miss, I know it!

Miss Brown: I dare say, but I said 'Hands up'. Right Joannne, start us off, will you?

Joanne: Fives into six, miss.

Miss Brown: Yes, go on.

Joanne: One

Miss Brown: Yes, it goes once. Then what?

Joanne: How do you mean, miss?

Miss Brown: What do we do next?

Mark: [*Hand up as if in agony*] Oh, miss, miss!

Miss Brown: All right, Mark, I know you know.

Tracey: [*To* **Mark**] Big head!

Linda: I know, too.

Miss Brown: Very well, Linda, go on with it. Watch, Joanne!

Linda: Put your one on top, say 'one five's five', say 'six take five leaves one', and then we – then we –

Miss Brown: Right, Linda. Who knows what we do?

All: [*Except* **Darren**] Bring the eight down.

Miss Brown: Yes, indeed. Darren Wildgoose, I didn't hear you.

Darren: What, miss?

Miss Brown: What is it we do, Darren? [*Pause*] Well?

Darren: Divide it, miss. [*Class giggles*]

Miss Brown: Darren Wildgoose, haven't you been listening?

Darren: Not much, miss.

Miss Brown: Well, you're a very silly boy. Follow what we're doing, and answer properly next time I ask you. Very well, here's the eight. And what now, Linda?

Linda: Fives into eighteen go three. Put three on top. Say 'three fives are fifteen', eight take five leaves three, one take one leaves nothing.

Miss Brown: Yes, Linda. What is it, Stephen?

Stephen: Why do we do it this daft way?

Miss Brown: Well, I know it's rather complicated, but it will help you with long division, you'll see. [*There are scrabbling noises at the back*] Whatever's going on? Darren Wildgoose?

Darren: Nothing, miss.

Miss Brown: What is it we do now, Darren?

Darren: Do where?

Miss Brown: Do on the board with our sum! Darren, what is the matter with you?

Glenroy: Miss, he dropped it.

Miss Brown: I wasn't speaking to you, Glenroy.

Glenroy: But he dropped it. . . .

Cheryl: Yes, miss, he did. It's rolled away!

Tracey: John Cavendish has put it in his pocket!

John: Miss, I haven't.

Tracey: Ooh, you liar! [*A conker drops on to the floor*]

Miss Brown: Quietly, everyone. What's all this about? Bring that thing here to me, Denise.

All: Miss, it's his conker!

Miss Brown: A conker? I've told you before about messing around with conkers in class. I'll have to keep it this time, Darren.

[*There is a general cry of protest*]

Glenroy: But miss, it's his three-hundred-and-sixer!

Miss Brown: His what?

Stephen: It's his, miss, it's brilliant!

Glenroy: It's the champ!

Joanne: It's won all the rest!

Miss Brown: Beaten all the rest, you mean. Quiet, everyone. Well, it looks like any old conker to me, and I think it's time I took care of it.

All: Oh, miss!

Miss Brown: Now, come along, Darren. You can finish this sum off for us. Here's the chalk. You can do it on the board.

Mark: Oh, miss, can I do it please? I know it!

Miss Brown: No. Darren's doing it.

Darren: Miss, I can't reach.

Mark: I could reach!

Joanne: Miss, isn't he little!

Miss Brown: That's quite enough, Mark. And that's not a nice thing to say, Joanne.

Michelle: I'm little too, aren't I, Miss Brown?

Miss Brown: Yes, yes, Michelle, you are. Come along, Darren. You can stand on that chair. We're doing the take-away part. [*He takes a spare chair, puts it by the blackboard and stands on it. Pause*]

Glenroy: [*In a loud whisper from the back*] Put a three!

Miss Brown: Glenroy Williams, quiet please! Yes, Darren?

Darren: How can I put a three? There's a three there already.

Miss Brown: Oh, really, Darren, that's a different three. I think you'd better come to me afterwards. And will you please remember. . . .

Glenroy: [*Urgently, looking out of the window*] Miss!

Miss Brown: Quiet, please! When you are in this classroom you concentrate on what we are doing. . . .

Glenroy: But, miss, miss look there. . . .

Miss Brown: Glenroy Williams, you are being impossible this morning!

Glenroy: But miss, something extraordinary is happening!

[*The children peer out of the window*]

Miss Brown: Something extraordinarily nasty will happen in a moment if you can't sit still and listen to me! [*The noise of the spaceship is heard, getting louder and louder*] Good heavens! [*Shrieks, squeals, and cries from the children*] Don't get up children! Stay where you are!

[*The hum suddenly stops.* **Miss Brown** *and the class freeze like statues*]

Leader: Nogwog tiddle eek choc zag!

Spaceman: Keep your seats. Do not fear. We wish you no harm.

[*The class comes to life again*]

Miss Brown: Eek!

Denise: Don't worry miss, it's only spacemen!

John: Hey, Mark, look at his suit.

Cheryl: Have they landed in our yard, then?

Glenroy: Yes, that's what I tried to tell her.

Tracey: Do you think Miss Brown'll faint?

Joanne: Shall I hold your hand, Miss?

Mark: Can we get their autographs?

[*All at once*]

[**Darren** *climbs down off the chair and sits on it*]

Leader: Mop clab itzo, bong hip chippie!

Spaceman: Quiet everyone! Silence all! Where is your leader? Which is your leader?

Miss Brown: Well I – well, I – I suppose – Would you like to see the Head? John, pop out and get Mr Stuart, will you, love?

[**John** *goes out*]

Spaceman: [*Looking round*] The Leader – which is the Leader?

Miss Brown: Well I'm the teacher of course. . . .

Spaceman: Teacher? What is teacher? I do not know teacher. Ah! Yes – teacher. You cannot be the teacher you are too big.

Miss Brown: Pardon?

Spaceman: Teacher is Leader?

Miss Brown: Er, yes. . . .

Spaceman: Leader is not big. A Leader is never big. No Leaders are big. He is my Leader there. Look at him. Is he big? [*Points to* **Leader**, *who has been walking about examining the children closely. They keep a wary eye on him*]

Miss Brown: No, well he's not, but. . . .

Spaceman: I do what he tells me because I am bigger. The bigger ones are servants. The biggest ones are slaves. You are the size of a servant.

Miss Brown: Oh!

Linda: Oh, poor Miss Brown!

[**John** *comes in*]

Miss Brown: Oh, John! What did Mr Stuart say?

John: He says he can't come unless it's urgent.

Miss Brown: But it is urgent! Didn't you explain?

John: I couldn't think how to put it, miss.

Leader: [*Suddenly*] Twerpy chink ork und penny-wood!

Spaceman: My Leader says we have come to talk to all these others, not to you, Big Servant. We are looking for a group of small important leaders. We saw your room from far off. Now we seek the smallest of all. He must be the Leader.

Leader: [*Up to each child in turn*] Soppit. Soppiter. Soppitest!

Cheryl: What's he doing?

Mark: He's testing to find the smallest, isn't he?

Tracey: [*To* **Spaceman**] Sir, Darren Wildgoose is smallest.

All: It's right, he is. Yes, it's Darren – come on, Darren. Go on, Darren. Let him see you.

Darren: [*Shyly*] It's probably me that's smallest, sir. [*He stands up on the chair again*]

Leader: [*Delighted*] Hukah! Smango! Termants!

Spaceman: Ah! Great Leader, we bow to you! We have found the one we seek! [*To* **Miss Brown**] There, do you see, Big One? He is far smaller even than my chief.

Miss Brown: Well, yes I see, but it's ridiculous. I mean it's absurd, he's just a child –

Leader: Roppertop!

Spaceman: Silence, Big One!

Miss Brown: Well, I really can't stay here and listen to all this rubbish about Darren Wildgoose being a Leader, it's. . . .

Spaceman: Quiet!

Leader: [*Pointing a raygun at* **Miss Brown**] Ropper-top, dibble choke!

All: Oooh!

Denise: Oh, look what he's done to Miss Brown! She can't move! Can you move, miss? She can't! Miss, can you speak? She can't speak!

Mark: Hey, is she dead?

Linda: 'Course she's not dead, she's sitting up, isn't she?

Stephen: She's been zapped. It won't hurt her.

Leader: Flip cam breck in trig mor?

Spaceman: My leader is talking to you, smallest one. He cannot speak your language but he can understand what you say. He wants you to explain your earthly habits to us.

Darren: Er - you what?

Glenroy: Go on, Darren, just try it!

Michelle: Please sir. I'm as small as Darren, look!

Mark: Sit down, nutter, they don't want a girl.

Tracey: 'Course they want a girl, that's nothing to do with it, big head.

Spaceman: You small girl may stand by his side, but

you are not so small as he.

Tracey: There you are, Michelle, you climb on a chair too, love. [*She helps* **Michelle** *to climb up on to her own chair. Aside to* **Mark***, bitterly*] Boys!

Leader: [*Looking closely at* **Glenroy***, who is black*] Hoop nippir calswot armo shobble!

Stephen: Hey, Glenroy, he's going on at you now!

Glenroy: [*To* **Spaceman**] What's the matter with him, sir?

Spaceman: My leader says he likes your colour.

Glenroy: That's nice of him.

Spaceman: The pale people in this room look ill, he says.

Glenroy: Yes, my dad says that too. There's quite a few of us round here if you take a good look.

Spaceman: But you are much bigger than these small ones. Black is beautiful, but small is important.

Glenroy: Hey, suppose you meet my sister Lucy? She's only 2. She's beautiful and important.

Spaceman: Quiet now. Smallest one, we are waiting for your words.

Darren: Well, go on then. Ask me something.

Leader: Rippety quid shotto wopple humdig?

Spaceman: My Leader says what do you do in this room?

Darren: Er. . . .

All: [*Whisper*] Say we learn, Darren, go on.

Darren: We learn things.

Spaceman: Ah, you learn! I have learned your language. What do you learn?

Mark: Go on, Darren, tell him about maths.

Joanne: – and art.

John: – and PE.

Linda: – and home economics.

Leader: Hippy tweek 'home economics'?

Spaceman: What is home economics?

Darren: Well, it's when you make jam tarts. And PE's when you climb up things and jump off. And art's pictures, and English is stories and maths is sums. And that's it really.

Denise: Tell him about projects.

Darren: Well, projects is – when you look things up in one book and write them down in another book.

Mark: Sir, he's daft. That's not it, daftie. Sir, he doesn't know. I'll show you my project book on World War Two, sir. He only did rabbits.

Tracey: Shut up being cheeky, Mark Tyler, or he'll zap you like he did miss.

Leader: Hippy tweek oodle hommer taffle plonk?

Spaceman: What is this written on the green wood?

Denise: What greenwood?

Linda: Silly, he means the blackboard! Blackboards are all green nowadays. Go on, tell him it's a sum, Darren.

Darren: Yes, it's a multiplication sum.

All: A division sum!

Tracey: Sir, he's dozy!

Leader: Hippy tweek 'sum'?

Spaceman: What is a sum?

Darren: Well, it's that on there with all those numbers and things.

Leader: Cloppy twang tatter?

Spaceman: My leader asks one of you to say what it is for.

Joanne: [*After a pause*] Tell him.

Denise: I don't know what to say, do you?

Mark: I know.

Tracey: Well then, what is it for, clever?

Linda: Well, it's for If. If you're papering a room, or something.

Mark: That's area, daftie. That's what Miss Brown said about area.

Linda: Well, it's the same, isn't it? It's all sums.

Leader: Daggle argle pitter hip nit ooper?

Spaceman: Why do you learn these sums? Why do you learn these sums?

Mark: Sir, I know. It's so you can get your O-levels and get to college and your mum'll be proud of you, like my sister Mary.

Spaceman: What is this Ole Vello?

Mark: Not 'Ole Vello'. O-level! Oh, it's hopeless talking to you!

Stephen: Anyway, that's not the reason you do sums. If you couldn't do sums you couldn't build buildings or make aeroplanes or run the trains or get anything right, my dad says.

Spaceman: How do sums build buildings?

Stephen: Well, you see, you have to work out the number of bricks, and how high it is, and when it's going to collapse and all stuff like that.

Spaceman: Do you know how we build in our land? You think of your building, and you think how tall it must be, you see it in your mind's eye, you clear a space and collect your material, and next thing – there it is, built by thought waves!

[*There is a stunned silence*]

John: Sounds all right where they come from.

Tracey: Mr Stuart's coming!

[*Enter* **Headmaster**]

Mr Stuart: Now, Miss Brown, you wanted to see me? Good Lord! Who are you, sir?

Leader: Roppertop, steepleganger!

Spaceman: Silence, Big One! Why do you burst into this place?

Mr Stuart: I beg your pardon? I'm the Headmaster!

My name's Stuart. Miss Brown, who are these people?

Denise: It's no use, sir, she's zapped.

Mr Stuart: Quiet, girl! Whatever is 'zapped'?

Leader: Roppertop!

Spaceman: Silence, Big One!

Mr Stuart: Look here, sir, I demand to know. . . .

Spaceman: Let your small ones speak. Listen to what your small ones have to say.

Mr Stuart: Oh, well - Linda Cawthorne, please explain to me what is going on here.

Linda: Well, sir, these gentlemen have come from Outer Space, and they've zapped Miss Brown and they think Darren Wildgoose is the greatest, and they're asking us all about school, sir.

Glenroy: They wish us no harm, sir, they said.

Mr Stuart: Thank you very much, Glenroy. When I want your opinion I'll ask for it.

Glenroy: [*To himself*] Might do you a power of good.

Mr Stuart: What are you muttering, lad?

Spaceman: Listen to this small person, Big One!

Mr Stuart: [*Taken aback*] Oh - well - very well. What is it, Glenroy?

Glenroy: Well, if I were you I wouldn't cross them. They're powerful kind of people.

Mark: See, sir, they really zapped Miss Brown, look!

Glenroy: They might even zap you, sir. Strikes me

we'd better do what they say, and we'll help you get out of the mess somehow, sir.

Mr Stuart: Er – yes I see. . . .

Mark: Sir, I've got an idea. Why not get Mr Driscoll?

Denise: Oh, yes, he's ever so good at putting things right. Like the time when there was all sick all over the girls' toilet.

Stephen: Yes, I bet we could – like – tell him, you know, sir, tip him a wink. [*Trying to be discreet*]

Spaceman: What is 'tip him a wink'?

Stephen: Nothing. We'd just like you to meet the school caretaker, Mr Driscoll, because, well, he is a bit of a slave like you said big people should be.

Tracey: He'll do you if he hears that, Stephen Marshall.

Mr Stuart: [*Suddenly irritated*] Get down from that chair, Darren Wildgoose! Why are you standing up there anyway?

Darren: See, sir, they think I'm the boss like. [*He gets down*]

Mr Stuart: How very stupid of them!

Leader: Ooper toodle vick chip dilk?

Spaceman: Why do you always interrupt? Why can you not keep quiet for one moment?

Mark: Hey, Steve, 's what he says to us.

Spaceman: Tell me, smallest one, why do you do as this Big One bids you?

Darren: Well, you have to, don't you? I mean, like – well, he's headmaster, isn't he?

Tracey: Mr Driscoll's outside.

Denise: Oh, sir, me and Cheryl Bates'll get him. He's our friend. [*They go to the door.* **Denise** *calls outside*] Miss Brown says will you just come in here a moment, please Mr Driscoll?

[**Mr Driscoll** *enters*]

Mr Driscoll: Were you wanting me? Oh!

Denise: Mr Driscoll, these are two gentlemen from Outer Space, and they'd like to say Hello to you.

Mr Driscoll: Well, I'll go to the foot of our stairs!

Mr Stuart: Mr Driscoll. . . .

Leader: [*Silencing him*] Roppertop!

Mr Stuart: One of you will have to tell him.

Stephen: Right, sir. Well you see, Mr Driscoll. . . .

Glenroy: [*With a heavy wink*] Hey, Mr Driscoll. You know about 999?

Mr Driscoll: Pardon?

Stephen: Yes! You know? 999? [*He winks very hard, several times*]

Mr Stuart: Quite right, quite right boys – well, Mr Driscoll?

Mr Driscoll: I don't think I follow, Mr Stuart.

Linda: Just think hard, Mr Driscoll. You see, Miss Brown's been zapped because she talked too much, and these gentlemen are ever so good at under-standing our language.

Cheryl: Yes, it's right, they are, Mr Driscoll.

Denise: So, like the boys said, 999, Mr Driscoll! [*The penny drops*]

Mr Driscoll: I think I get you now, love!

Spaceman: What is this 999?

Denise: Well, it's a kind of, like, a sort of magic number like, just to show you how fantastic we think you are, isn't it, Cheryl?

Cheryl: Yes, that's right.

Glenroy: [*Inspired*] Yes, come on now, kids, we all say it – 999.

All: 999!!!

Spaceman: Thank you. 999 to you, too.

Mr Driscoll: [*To* **Spaceman**] Excuse me, sir, will it be all right if I get on now?

Mark: Yes, you know, he's got his slave duties to do.

Spaceman: Certainly you may go. [**Mr Driscoll** *goes out*]

Leader: Honk tiddle twick nocker.

Spaceman: My leader is impatient. We have not yet fulfilled our mission. We wish to start peaceful games between this world and ours. What sport do you play in this place?

All the boys: Football!

Leader: Hippy tweek 'football'?

Spaceman: What is football?

[*All the boys try to explain at once*]

Denise: It's a boys' game, is football. Don't you want to know about something good like skipping, sir?

[*Hearty laughter from all the boys*]

All boys: Skipping!!

Stephen: He'd look great, wouldn't he, skipping round the moon craters?

Spaceman: Our game is a game of single combat. It is called Woblongy. Each man holds a round object hanging from a chain. That is the Woblong. By might and skill the rivals try to shatter each other's weapon, and finally one and one alone triumphs. He is now the supreme champion and his Woblong is therefore priceless.

John: Whatever's he on about?

Leader: [*Sternly*] Roppertop!

Spaceman: Do not mock our noble sport!

Darren: [*Slowly*] Hey. Just wait a minute.

Spaceman: Yes, Smallest One? What is it you have to say?

Darren: [*Still slowly*] I think I get it. . . . It makes sense to me. . . . Hang on a bit. . . . Excuse me, miss.

Tracey: Hey, look he's lifting up Miss Brown's zapped fingers!

John: It's his conker!

Cheryl: Hey, it's our Darren's three-hundred-and-sixer!

Darren: You haven't got that thingy you were talking about on you, have you, sir?

Spaceman: My Leader guards it – our Champion Woblong.

Darren: Because, you see, this is my conker. And it's a lot like what you said, sir, what it does. And it's won three hundred and six of them battles like you said, sir.

Spaceman: Three hundred and six!

Leader: [*Astonished*] Tracker jock!

Darren: Yes, sir, honest.

Denise: Yes, it's right, he has.

Stephen: He's brilliant at it, and that conker's the greatest!

Spaceman: Our Champion Woblong has won two hundred and eighty-eight times. Yet it is renowned throughout our planet.

Leader: Slamp derry diddle dong imp supple twee.

Spaceman: My leader wishes your conker to prove its great worth.

Darren: All right then. I don't mind.

[*The **Leader** takes the Woblong out of his pocket. It looks very much like a silver-plated conker*]

Spaceman: Are you ready? Go!

Denise: Go on, Darren, you can do it! Beat him kid, beat him!

[*They all make suitable exclamations of encouragement. By the end they are chanting 'DAR-REN, DAR-REN' in unison.* **Darren** *wins the battle and they all cheer*]

Leader: Yam whipple alley skip! (Praise for the Victor).

Spaceman: Oh, great warrior, you can stay here no longer! Come with us to our planet where you will receive great honours.

Darren: Will I? Will I really?

Denise: Oh, Darren, you wouldn't would you? What'll your mam say?

Darren: She'll miss me, but well, like they say, it's an opportunity, isn't it?

Mr Stuart: No, no, no, boy. I forbid it! It's impossible, it's unthinkable – I'll be blamed! Your mother will never believe. . . .

Stephen: Oh, go on sir, we'll explain.

Mr Stuart: No, Darren, no! You can't sacrifice yourself!

Darren: But I'm not, am I sir? I mean like they said, I'll be famous, it'll be great. I mean I'm not much good at sums or at football but I've always been champion at conkers. There's not much chance of earning a living at that down here, is there now?

Linda: Oh, sir, it's his big chance!

Denise: It's like 'Opportunity Knocks'!

Spaceman: Do you wish for friends to come with you? That little one or the dark one there?

Darren: Well, I'd rather not take Michelle Benson. She's a bit dumb.

Michelle: I don't care. I'm going to grow up and have a baby, like our Sylvia.

Darren: What about it, Glen?

Glenroy: Thanks all the same, but I plan to drive a bus like my dad.

[*Police sirens are heard in the distance*]

Mark: Get going, you nutter! They're coming for them!

Linda: They'll stop you!

Darren: Right. Just a minute, I'll just have a word with my cousin. Hey our Cheryl, tell me mam I'll be all right, OK?

Cheryl: Right, Darren. All the best.

Stephen: Listen, the siren's stopped.

All: Quick, quick, they're coming – get on with it – etc.

Leader: Zip – zip – zip!

Spaceman: Come here, Smallest One, here to us. With our hands on your shoulders you will be filled with our power.

Glenroy: See you Darren. Good-bye, good-bye.

[*Spaceship noises start again, quietly at first, but rising to a loud throb*]

Darren: Darren the Conkerer! Fancy me famous! [*The* **Spacemen** *make for the door*] Hey – wait for me!

The end

Politics and Terror
Willy Russell

Characters
George
Chris
Tommo

Politics and Terror

A young kid, in short trousers, is sitting on a low wall. He is chewing and staring into the distance, beyond the heat haze. He suddenly crouches low, produces his imaginary 'pistol' and picks off three baddies. He returns the gun to his belt. He sits and continues his chewing.

*Behind him we see another kid (**George**) appear. He creeps up, and as he does so he unpins an equally imaginary 'grenade' and lobs it at **Chris**. He waits a moment before making the sound of the explosion.*

George: [*As* **Chris** *looks round*] You're dead.

Chris: No I'm not.

George: Yis y'are. I got y' with a grenade, at point blank range.

Chris: Well –

George: Well what?

Chris: Well, that means you're dead as well, cos you didn't move out of range.

George: I don't have to. A grenade wouldn't injure me. I've got super powers.

Chris: Which ones?

George: All of them. I'm indestructible.

Chris: No, y'not. None of the Super Heroes is in-destructible.

George: The Hulk is.

Chris: No, he's not. Even Superman's not indes-tructible an' he's the most indestructible Super Hero there is. But even Superman can't face Kryptonite.

George: [*Shrugging*] D'you live round here?

Chris: [*Indicating*] Down there.

George: What y' doin' round here?

Chris: I've been the shops.

George: What for?

Chris: [*Immediately defensive*] Nothin'.

George: [*Goes into the sound of a police wah-wah siren. Suddenly stops*] Gis a sweet.

Chris: I haven't got any. [**George** *looks at him.* **Chris** *turns away and begins to make the sound of a bleep phone*]

George: Which shop did y' go to?

Chris: Supermarket.

George: What for?

Chris: What?

George: What did y' go the supermarket for?

Chris: For me mam. I was on a message.

George: What did y' get?

Chris: Nott'n. It was closed.

George: [*Sceptical, but not to be put off*] It's dead lucky for you it was closed.

Chris: Why?

George: There's rats in that supermarket. An' y' know if y' bought somethin' from there, somethin' to eat, like sweets, an' y' ate them, y'd get the fever.

Chris: The fever?

George: Yeh. Y' die if y' catch the fever. There's three kids died from our street, y' know.

Chris: [*Pause*] Y' wouldn't die if y' just ate one sweet from there, though. Would y'?

George: Y' would. Y' don't even have to eat them. Just havin' them in y' pocket – that's enough. The germs travel up t' y' mouth. They fly. It's best if y' throw them away.

Chris: [*Looking at him*] Listen, y' know somethin' eh?

George: What?

Chris: Isn't it lucky for me the supermarket was closed.

George: [*Disgusted*] I seen you chewin'.

Chris: Y' never, cos I wasn't chewin'.

George: Y' were. I seen y' goin' like that. [*Exaggerated chew*]

Chris: I wasn't chewin' nott'n though. I was tryin' t'

bite off a piece of loose skin in me gum. Like that. [*Shows him the chewing action*]

George: [*Pause*] I get that sometimes, inside me mouth.

Chris: Yeh, well so do I.

George: Look. [*Opens his mouth.* **Chris** *peers in*]

Chris: Oh yeh . . . I can see it. That's just like mine was.

George: Let's have a look. [**Chris** *opens his mouth.* **George** *peers in.* **George** *suddenly pointing, accusing*] See . . . I told y' you had sweets, there's all yellow over y' tongue. . . . You've got sweets.

Chris: I haven't got sweets. I had some, but that was the last one. An' I didn't get it from the supermarket, I got it from the paper shop. [*He gets up to go*] I'm goin'. [*Making police wah-wah sound before zooming off*]

George: Where?

Chris: Home

George: Down there?

Chris: Yeh.

George: Y' know who's down there?

Chris: [*Coming back a step*] Who?

George: Tommo!

Chris: Tommo? [**George** *nods*] Tommo isn't down there. Tommo got sent away. Tommo's in a home cos of bullyin' little kids an' murderin' dogs.

George: Look. [*Points*]

Chris: Is that Tommo?

George: [*Nods*] Tommo's back now. [*He walks away leaving* **Chris** *worried and anxious, gawping down the road*] With an air pistol as well. [**George** *suddenly makes the Tarzan call.* **Chris** *moves across to him*]

Chris: Tarzan's on telly tonight, y' know.

George: The Lord of the Jungle, I know.

Chris: Y' know Tarzan, all livin' things are his friends.

George: I'll bet Tarzan wouldn't be Tommo's friend.

Chris: He would. Tarzan says all livin' things are his friends.

George: But what about Tommo? All livin' things are Tommo's enemies. Especially when they've got sweets. [*Pause*] I thought you were goin' home.

Chris: [*Looking anxiously down the street*] Erm. . . . I forgot, me mam won't be home yet.

George: Y' know if I've got some sweets, I share them, with everyone.

Chris: Do y'?

George: Yeh. Cos that's what Jesus says y' should do. When I've got sweets I share them.

Chris: [*Unimpressed*] An' another thing Jesus said was if y' tell lies y' go to hell when y' die.

George: What's that bulge in your pocket?

Chris: What? That? It's me hankie. I've got a cold. [*Sniffs*] I don't believe in Jesus and God, me dad says. [*Sniffs. Wheeling*] I'm goin' now. Tarar.

George: [*Standing and pointing down the street*] There's Tommo, look.

Chris: [*Stopping*] Where?

George: There.

Chris: That's not Tommo.

George: [*Holding up pretend binoculars*]. It is. An' there's three little kids there as well. They're cryin'. Tommo's got them. [**Chris** *begins to sniffle.* **George** *begins to laugh*] What's up?

Chris: I've gorra get home. Me mam said I've gorra get in before dinner time, cos she's goin' out with our Maureen. But I can't go home . . . not with Tommo there.

George: Take the short cut.

Chris: [*Stops crying. Hopeful*] Which short cut?

George: It's a secret.

Chris: What? Go on . . . tell us.

George: I can't. You've gorra be in the Indian Trackin' Gang if y' wanna know all the short cuts.

Chris: Well I'll join.

George: Y' can't. You've got no sweets.

Chris: What?

George: Y' have to pay a load of sweets when y' join the Indian Trackin' Gang.

Chris: Well . . . well . . . well . . . let me join now an' I'll give y' some sweets the next time I see y'.

George: But I might never see y' again.

Chris: Y' will.

George: [*Shaking his head*] Not if you have to go down there, past Tommo. No one'll ever see you again. [*Craning to see down the road*] Ugh. . . . Look what Tommo's doin' to that little kid. . . .

Chris: [*Sneaking his hand into his pocket and then bending as if to pick something up*] Look what I've just found, on the floor. Look, I can join with these. [*He shows a few sweets*]

George: [*Taking them*] Nah. . . . Y' could if you'd found more. But this isn't enough. . . .

Chris: But that's all I found . . . that's all there were, on the floor.

George: Have another look. There might be some more there.

Chris: There won't be.

George: [*Looking*] Ugh . . . Tommo's gettin' dead mad with them kids.

Chris: [*Quickly bending to 'discover' more sweets*] Look . . . look. I found some more. . . . [*Giving them to George*] Where is it . . . tell me where the short cut is.

George: [*Shaking his head*] Not enough.

Chris: [*Nearly in tears*] But I haven't got any more. I mean, I mean I can't find any more. . . .

George: I'd tell y' if I could. But it's in the rules of the gang. It says y' have to give 'A load of sweets'.

Chris: You . . . you . . . y' just want all my sweets.

George: You haven't got any sweets, have y'?

Chris: The sweets I'm findin'.

George: I don't want sweets. What do I want sweets for. It's you. Y' wanna know the short cut, don't y'?

Chris: I've gorra get home. . . . I've got to.

George: [*Looking at the sweets in his hand*] Well this is nearly loads. Maybe if y' had another look y' could find some more.

Chris: [*Crying, frustrated. He turns and fishes the last of his sweets out of his pocket. Turns*] I found these. But I won't be able to find any more, I know I won't. You better tell me where that short cut is now. . . . Y' better had. . . .

George: [*Taking the sweets*] Come here. Y' see down by there, by the church, well if y' bunk over the wall y'll see an alley. . . . If you run down there it brings y' out dead quick by your flats. . . .

Chris: Over that wall. . . . There's no alley there.

George: Have you ever been over that wall?

Chris: No.

George: Well don't argue. . . . I have. An' y' better hurry up 'cos if Tommo moves further down this way you'll be seen, even takin' the short cut.

Chris: [*About to go*] I'm goin'. Listen . . . before I go . . . gis a sweet?

George: No way.

Chris: [*Laughing and pointing*] Well well . . . you're gonna die. . . . You're gonna get the fever . . . cos I bought them sweets in that supermarket! [*Laughing*]

George: Well . . . there's no alley behind that wall either. [*Laughs*]

[**Chris's** *laugh fades. He turns suddenly and runs.* **George** *is beaming. Then a Webley air pistol appears, followed by* **Tommo,** *a girl.* **George** *suddenly sobers*]

George: Er, hiya, Tommo. [**Tommo** *glares at him*] What y' doin'? Y' watchin' Tarzan on the telly tonight?

Tommo: Tarzan isn't on tonight.

George: He is.

Tommo: No he's not. . . . I shot him this mornin'. The Hulk's dead as well. Have you got sweets?

George: Sweets? Me? I got no sweets. Honest. . . .

The end

All Friends Together

Tim Shields

Characters
Mr Jenkins
Mrs Jenkins
Iris Jenkins
The Postman
Siri
Sybil
Arthur
Anne Smith
Geoffrey Smith
Anthony
Frances
Guests

All Friends Together

---

1   At the breakfast table

Mr *and* **Mrs Jenkins** *sit at breakfast.* **Mr Jenkins** *spends most of his time reading.* **Mrs Jenkins** *is a large lady, who talks loudly and deliberately.*

Between them sits **Iris**, *their one and lonely daughter. She looks very small and is ignored most of the time.* **Mrs Jenkins** *(of course) speaks first.*

Mrs Jenkins: George! It is high time we threw another party.

Mr Jenkins: Who at, dear?

Mrs Jenkins: You mean 'who for'.

Mr Jenkins: Four doesn't sound like a very big party.

Mrs Jenkins: George, you're not listening to me again.

Mr Jenkins: So I'm not. I'm sorry, dear.

Mrs Jenkins: Why aren't you listening to me, George?

Mr Jenkins: There's a man here, who put his whole house on wheels and turned it round to catch the morning sun.

Mrs Jenkins: That's no reason for you not to listen when I'm talking about something important.

Mr Jenkins: I wonder how many wheels we'd need to turn our house round. . . ?

Mrs Jenkins: Our house can stay right where it is. You know you get travel sick just pushing the hoover. Now the question is, who are we going to invite?

Mr Jenkins: Whoever you like, dear.

Mrs Jenkins: Don't be silly. If people only invited who they liked, there wouldn't be any parties.

Mr Jenkins: It would be nice and quiet.

Mrs Jenkins: Nonsense, we should all be bored to death.

Mr Jenkins: That would make it even quieter.

Mrs Jenkins: I'm not going to argue with you, George. If you don't want to help me, I shall go right ahead and make up the guest list on my own.

Mr Jenkins: I'll help you, dear. And what about Iris?

Mrs Jenkins: What about her?

Mr Jenkins: Perhaps she would like to ask someone?

Mrs Jenkins: Really?

Mr Jenkins: We could ask her.

Mrs Jenkins: All right, if you think so.

Mr Jenkins: Would you like to ask anyone, Iris?

[**Iris** *nods*]

Mrs Jenkins: Very well, you may ask one of your friends to come – provided that she is clean and well-behaved. [*A pause*]

Iris: I haven't got any friends. [*Another pause. Parents look at her*]

Mrs Jenkins: How absurd! Everyone has got friends. I've got friends. Your father's got friends. You must have friends.

Iris: I haven't.

Mrs Jenkins: What about Pauline and Jane and Susan and Janet and Rachel and Penelope and Fiona and Annabel and Marion and Sally and Carol and the one that looks like a ferret?

Iris: Julie Perkins.

Mrs Jenkins: Julie Perkins.

Iris: They're not friends. They just go to my school.

Mrs Jenkins: Well, if you don't want to ask anyone, that's your business.

Iris: But I *do* want to bring someone.

Mrs Jenkins: Who?

Iris: It'll be a surprise! [*She runs out*]

Mr Jenkins: There's a man here selling off plots of land on the moon, with permission to build three houses.

Mrs Jenkins: I told you we are not moving.

Mr Jenkins: Does Julie Perkins really look like a ferret?

2   Outside the front door

The **Postman** *arrives on his knees, dragging behind him a vast sack, bulging with angular packages. He is about to ring the front doorbell when* **Iris** *appears.*

Iris: Please don't ring the bell, you'll wake everybody up.

Postman: Is this number 10, The Close?

Iris: That's right.

Postman: Does a Miss . . . Jenkins live here?

Iris: Yes, that's me.

Postman: Are you expecting a parcel or six?

Iris: Yes.

Postman: These must be for you then.

Iris: I'll take them one at a time. You see, I want to get them inside without my parents seeing.

Postman: Ah, a surprise, is it?

Iris: Yes, sort of.

Postman: Well, I'd better give you a hand.

Iris: Thanks very much.

[**Iris** *and the* **Postman** *pick up a parcel each and tip-toe after each other through the front door. Then they return to collect the other parcels which they handle with the same show of silent secrecy.* **Iris** *looks at the* **Postman** *with gratitude*]

Iris: Thanks very much.

Postman: Not at all, miss.

Iris: I suppose you wouldn't like to come to a party, would you?

Postman: Beg your pardon?

Iris: Oh, nothing . . . just . . . 'bye. [*She gives him a quick wave and runs indoors. The* **Postman** *picks up his sack and gives the empty sack a powerful tug – with the inevitable result – he tumbles over*]

3 The living room

Thump thump clunk from overhead. Plaster flakes fall like snow upon **Mr Jenkins** *as he sits in an armchair, reading his paper.* **Mrs Jenkins** *enters.*

Mr Jenkins: It says here we're due for a white Christmas.

Mrs Jenkins: Really? What on earth is Iris up to now?

Mr Jenkins: Clog dancing, as far as I can tell.

Mrs Jenkins: You know, I sometimes worry about that girl.

Mr Jenkins: Do you, dear? Why is that?

Mrs Jenkins: Because I wonder if she's quite . . . right. She's always up in her room instead of sitting in front of the television. She doesn't play loud records, wear trendy clothes or plaster the walls of her room with pictures of pop stars. And she's so quiet and secretive.

Mr Jenkins: It's nice to be quiet.

Mrs Jenkins: It's unnatural to be as quiet as she is.

[*At this moment the hammering overhead becomes very loud*]

Mr Jenkins: I think she heard you.

Mrs Jenkins: I think it's time you had a fatherly chat with her.

Mr Jenkins: What's wrong with your having a nice motherly one? Woman to woman, and so on. . . .

Mrs Jenkins: We haven't got time to argue about that now. I've made a start on my party list, you see. [*She unravels a lengthy roll*] There are certain people I just have to invite.

Mr Jenkins: Who, for instance?

Mrs Jenkins: The Bakers, for a start. And if I ask the Bakers I have to ask the Browns - and if I ask the Browns I have to ask the Smiths - and if I ask the Smiths I have to ask the Joneses - and if I ask the Joneses -

Mr Jenkins: All right, all right. Look, there's a man here who ate a hundred and thirteen pork pies at one sitting.

Mrs Jenkins: That reminds me - what shall we have to eat?

Mr Jenkins: Anything - so long as it's not sausages on sticks again.

Mrs Jenkins: Well, we can't have a cold rice salad, because Sally made one. We can't have open sandwiches, because we had them at Molly Brown's.

And we can't have chicken wings because I can't cook them like Ruby Jones.

Mr Jenkins: So what are we having?

Mrs Jenkins: Sausages on sticks.

Mr Jenkins: Whatever you say, dear.

Mrs Jenkins: I shall have to have a new dress.

Mr Jenkins: What's wrong with your red one?

Mrs Jenkins: I wore that at the Smiths' anniversary party. And I can't wear the green one with fur because –

Mr Jenkins: Very well, dear, buy a new dress.

Mrs Jenkins: Right. Now will you go upstairs and stop Iris before she brings the ceiling down?

Mr Jenkins: She is half your daughter, isn't she?

Mrs Jenkins: The half that's making all that noise is not my half.

Mr Jenkins: My goodness, there's a woman here who lost so much weight that she can't go out in a high wind.

4 Iris's room

She has just finished making a life-size doll which now stands in the middle of the room.

Iris: [*Reading aloud from the instruction book*] 'When you have assembled your new friend, it is time to get her to speak. You just ask her a question and the built-in taperecorder will reply. . . .' Let's see if it works. Er, what's your name?

Doll: Siri

Iris: Siri? That's an unusual name. Would you like to come to a party?

Siri: I certainly would!

Iris: It might be rather boring – it's mostly grown-ups.

Siri: I'm rather good with grown-ups. I won't be bored, you wait and see.

[*There is a knock on the door*]

Mrs Jenkins: [*Outside*] Iris – is there someone in there?

Iris: No, mother! [**Iris** *rushes about the room, tidying up traces of the doll, and trying to find somewhere to hide her*]

Mrs Jenkins: Why is this door locked?

Iris: It's not locked, mother.

Mrs Jenkins: Then why can't I open it?

Iris: [*Kicking boxes under her bed*] I've no idea.

Mrs Jenkins: It must be locked.

Iris: Wait a minute. I'll come over and give you a hand with it.

Mrs Jenkins: Well, hurry up.

Iris: I'm being as quick as I can. [*Finally stuffs* **Siri** *into the wardrobe and shuts the door. Last look round, then admits her mother*]

Mrs Jenkins: I just came to tell you that if you're coming to the party this evening, you must have a rest this afternoon.

Iris: All right, mother.

Mrs Jenkins: By the way, what state is your party dress in? [*She moves towards the wardrobe.* **Iris** *leaps to intercept her*]

Iris: It's quite all right, mother. I've just ironed it.

Mrs Jenkins: Have you invited anybody?

Iris: Yes. Nobody you know, though.

Mrs Jenkins: You've made a new friend specially?

Iris: As a matter of fact, I have.

Mrs Jenkins: I hope I like the look of her. See you later. And don't forget the afternoon nap!

[**Iris** *lies on the bed obediently.* **Mrs Jenkins** *tiptoes out. When her mother has gone* **Iris** *jumps up, runs to the door, locks it, listens a moment, then opens the door of the wardrobe.* **Siri** *emerges, wearing* **Iris's** *best dress*]

Siri: Hadn't you better get ready for the party?

Iris: You are wearing my dress!

Siri: Got to look my best, haven't I?

Iris: I'm not sure I want you to come now.

Siri: Changed your mind?

Iris: I don't think you would enjoy it.

Siri: Because all your parents' boring old friends will

be oo-ing and coo-ing? 'My, how you've grown' – 'How
are we getting on at school?' – 'Isn't that a pretty little
dress'. . . .

Iris: What do you expect from grown-ups? They don't
know any better.

Siri: I suppose you want to impress them so they'll
think you're A Nice Little Girl?

Iris: We have to be polite.

Siri: You're afraid I'll let you down, aren't you, in
front of all those posh people.

Iris: No –

Siri: You're afraid I'll speak what's in your mind,
aren't you?

Iris: What's in my mind is my own business. [*She
turns on her heel, and nips out through the door,
locking it behind her*]

Siri: Some friend you are!

5   The party

Food and drink are laid out on the sideboard. **Mr** *and*
Mrs Jenkins *await their guests.* **Mrs Jenkins** *is all
aglow and aglitter with excitement and jewellery.* **Mr
Jenkins** *has thrown on a suit and is still reading a
paper.*

Mrs Jenkins: George, will you ever stop reading that
newspaper?

Mr Jenkins: Yes, dear – when I've finished it.

Mrs Jenkins: But our guests will be here any minute.

Mr Jenkins: Right you are.

Mrs Jenkins: Do you think there's enough food?

Mr Jenkins: There always is. We'll be eating little curly sandwiches for a fortnight. It's the liquor we run out of. Your friends soak it up like walking sandbags.

Mrs Jenkins: Where is Iris?

Mr Jenkins: I expect she'll be down in a minute.

Mrs Jenkins: She hasn't told me who she's bringing.

Mr Jenkins: Perhaps she isn't bringing anyone?

Mrs Jenkins: Oh, yes she is. She's invited a new friend that she made recently.

Mr Jenkins.   Made a friend? Our Iris is growing up!

Mrs Jenkins: Not too quickly, I hope.

Mr Jenkins: My goodness, there's a man here who cuts down on petrol by driving to work on his lawn-mower.

[*There is a knock at the door.* **Mrs Jenkins** *fixes her face in a smile. The first couple of guests arrive. They are identical with the next batch. All the guests look alike*]

Mrs Jenkins: Sybil – Arthur – how lovely to see you.

Sybil: Good evening, Martha, dear – George – and where's my darling little Iris? [*Spying her out*] Ah,

there she is. . . . Haven't you got a kiss for your Auntie
Sybil? [**Iris** *suffers an embrace*]

Arthur: My, isn't she looking grown-up?

Iris: [*Trying hard to do her duty*] Would you like a
sausage?

Sybil: Isn't that sweet?

Arthur: Are you our little waitress for the day?

[*Everyone laughs. Sausages are popped into mouths*]

Arthur: And how are we getting on at school –
working hard?

Iris: Yes, I think so.

Sybil: I can't get over how she's grown. I can remember you when you were that high. . . . [*Demonstrates with flattened hand*] She looks more like you
every day, Martha.

Arthur: Won't be long before she has a string of boys
in tow, eh?

Mrs Jenkins: Gracious, heaven forbid! [*Pause,
during which a bumping noise is heard from overhead*] What was that?

Sybil: It sounded to me like a dog.

Arthur: Yes, that's what I thought.

Mrs Jenkins: Iris, have you got a dog in your room?

Iris: [*Trying to change the subject*] Would anybody
like another sausage?

Mrs Jenkins: Iris. . . ?

Iris: No, mother, of course I haven't got a dog in my room.

[*The next identical couple arrive to stop further questioning*]

Mrs Jenkins: Anne – Geoffrey – how lovely to see you.

Anne: Good evening, Martha darling – George – and how's my little Iris? Have you got a kiss for your Auntie Anne? My, doesn't she look grown-up?

Iris: [*Striving very hard indeed*] Would you like a sausage?

Anne: Isn't that delightful?

Geoffrey: Are you our little waitress for the day?

[*Laughter. Sausages popped in*]

Geoffrey: How are we getting on at school – working hard?

Iris: Yes, I think so.

Anne: I can't get over how she's grown. I can remember you when you were that high. . . . [*Demonstrates*] She looks more like you every day, Martha.

Geoffrey: Won't be long before she has a string of boys in tow, eh?

Mrs Jenkins: Gracious, heaven forbid!

[*Pause, during which crashes are heard from overhead.* **Siri** *is trying to escape from the bedroom*]

Mrs Jenkins: What is that? [*There is a final loud crash as* **Siri** *breaks the bedroom door open. Another couple arrive*] Anthony - Frances - how delightful you could come. [*The couple are hardly inside the room before* **Iris** *shuts the door and stands in front of it*] Iris, what are you doing now?

Iris: Nothing, mother. I was just looking after the door. It didn't look very safe. [*The door is hammered from the opposite side*] There you are, it sounds as if it could crash open any minute.

Mrs Jenkins: Do you think someone is trying to come in?

Iris: No, - I didn't hear anyone ring the bell, did you? [*The bell now gives a series of deafening rings*] Is that the telephone?

Siri: [*Shouting from behind the door*] It's about time you lot opened this door!

Mrs Jenkins: There *is* somebody.

Iris: That could be anybody - you don't want to let in just anybody.

Mrs Jenkins: Open the door.

Iris: I don't think we should.

Mrs Jenkins: George - tell your daughter to open the door.

Mr Jenkins: Open the door for your mother, dear.

Iris: You are making a big mistake. [**Siri** *starts banging again*] You'll regret it.

[**Siri** *starts pushing her way in as* **Iris** *struggles to*

*hold the door shut. All the guests look on in some
amazement. After a long struggle, Siri flings the door
open, pushing Iris into her mother]*

Siri: [*Very pleasantly*] Good evening, everyone! [*Iris
grabs another tray of food and tries to escape, but
Siri stops her*] Are you our little waitress for the day?
Isn't that sweet! My, how you've grown! You'll soon
have a string of boys in tow. . . . [*Siri takes a handful
of snacks and drifts among the other guests, who
carry on chatting*]

Mrs Jenkins: Aren't you going to introduce me to
your friend, Iris?

Iris: She's not my friend – I don't know her at all.

Mrs Jenkins: Well, she obviously knows you very
well.

Iris: That's what worries me.

[**Siri** *arrives back to hear this remark*]

Siri: I'll have another of your sausages if you don't
mind, old pal. [*Grabs some*] And you must be Mrs
Jenkins, I presume?

Mrs Jenkins: Yes, I am. Pleased to meet you . . .
er. . . ?

Siri: Siri

Mrs Jenkins: Siri? That's an unusual name.

Siri: I'm rather an unusual person.

Mrs Jenkins: Oh, really? [*She doesn't quite know*

what to say] Well, this is my husband. George, this is Siri.

Mr Jenkins: Siri? That's an unusual name. You're a friend of Iris's, I gather?

Siri: In an unusual sort of way, yes, I am.

Mrs Jenkins: Would you like to meet a few of our friends, er, Siri?

Siri: Not particularly. They all look much of a muchness, if you ask me.

Mr Jenkins: That's very observant of you.

Mrs Jenkins: George, don't interrupt. You are always hogging the conversation. You must meet the Smiths. I'll go and get them. [*She hurries away.* **Iris** *whispers to* **Siri**]

Iris: Please don't do anything. . . .

Siri: Like what?

Iris: Or say anything.

Siri: You want me to enjoy myself, don't you?

Iris: I'll get into trouble afterwards if you don't behave.

Siri: Don't worry, friend, I'll take care of things.

Iris: Oh, must you?

[**Mrs Jenkins** *returns with the* **Smiths**, *one of the couples who arrived earlier*]

Mrs Jenkins: Anne – Geoffrey – I'd like you to meet a new friend of Iris's – Siri.

Anne: Siri? What an unusual name.

Siri: Yes, isn't it. Fancy your noticing.

[**Mrs Smith** *spies* **Iris** *holding her plate of sausages*]

Anne: Can I have just one more teensy-weensy one?

Siri: Don't you know when you've had enough, you great balloon?

[**Anne** *withdraws her hand, as if scalded*]

Anne: What did you say?

Geoffrey: Really, I don't think you should speak to a lady like that.

Siri: I wouldn't have spoken to her at all from choice. We were brought together by force.

Geoffrey: You have insulted my wife.

Siri: And you have fouled up the air by turning yourself into a walking chimney.

Geoffrey: Well, really!

Siri: Oh, don't waggle your hairy lip at me, you pompous old idiot.

[**Mrs Jenkins** *tries to change the subject*]

Mrs Jenkins: George, turn on the gramophone – let us have some dancing.

Mr Jenkins: What sort of music, dear...? [*Turns on player – it's a Jimmy Shand record*]

Mrs Jenkins: That will do.... Come along everybody

- it's time for some dancing. Take your partners quickly – we'll start with . . . a Gay Gordons! [*Rather surprised, the guests shuffle into position for the dance.* **Mrs Jenkins** *jollies them along*] Are we all ready now – we'll have the introduction again – right – off we go!

[*The dancing starts.* **Mrs Jenkins** *supervises,* **Mr Jenkins** *reads his paper,* **Iris** *keeps an eye on* **Siri**, *who watches from the sidelines. The dancing is clumsy and ludicrous, as people are still juggling with glasses and snacks, as well as partners. It has all started so abruptly that it is a struggle to catch up. But then* **Siri** *intervenes to make things more difficult*]

Siri: This is boring. Let's play it at the right speed.

[*The music doubles in tempo and volume. Couples are forced to accelerate. Parade, turn, spin, dance. Parade-turn-spin-dance*]

Mrs Jenkins: George, stop that!

Siri: [*Grabbing him for a dance*] Come on, Uncle George, time to live a little!

[**Mrs Jenkins** *fights her way towards the gramophone, but is hindered by the dancers, who scamper, fizz and pop. Some collapse, gasping for breath; some stand in a trance; one or two just dance on very fast until they go into an endless spin away out of sight, and have to be brought back to earth by their partners. By the time* **Mrs Jenkins** *manages to turn off the music, people, plates and party manners lie shattered.* **Mrs Jenkins** *storms up to* **Siri**]

Mrs Jenkins: How dare you do such a thing!

Anne: Yes, how dare you?

Geoffrey: Someone could have been killed!

[*The rest of the guests swarm around* **Siri** *venting their anger. 'Monstrous, dangerous, lunatic, stupid, irresponsible, no joke at all.'* **Siri** *suffers this for a moment or two then quells them with a mighty shout*]

Siri: All right! *All right!* That's enough of this nonsense. Shouting and screaming like a bunch of kids! Oh, you're such a pack of hypocrites! You all pretend to be great friends, but you really only come here to show off your new dresses, and guzzle as much free drink as you can hold. You don't care a fig for each other. You only stick together because it makes you feel safe, like sheep. [*They are indeed making bleating noises in their astonishment.* **Iris** *dives under the table in despair, but* **Siri** *continues in full spate*] But worst of all is the way you treat my friend, Iris. Look at her! Chuck her under the chin, pat her on the head when she performs like a Nice Little Girl. 'Isn't she growing up?' you say. What you mean is 'Isn't she well on the way to becoming one of us'. That must be the worst thing that could happen to anyone. It makes me sick. Iris, come out of there and stand up for yourself!

[*But* **Iris** *curls up even smaller, wishing she could vanish into air.*

After a stunned silence, the storm breaks. People buzz among themselves like angry bees. **Mr Jenkins** *takes refuge in his paper.* **Mrs Jenkins** *tries to look like a dignified hostess again*]

Mr Jenkins: Well I never – there's a man here who killed his father and married his mother.

Mrs Jenkins: Iris – will you ask – will you make that . . . person leave my house this instant!

Siri: Don't worry yourself, Mrs, I'm off. Cheerio, Iris. Any time you need a helping hand, just let me know. [**Siri** *saunters out*]

[**Iris** *puts her hands over her head and tries to disappear further. The lights dim down around her, leaving her pinpointed in her loneliness*]

6   Final scene

Three areas of light:
a   **Iris** *in her room*
b   **Mr** *and* **Mrs Jenkins** *sitting together*
c   *the front door, as in scene 2*

The doll lies in front of **Iris**, *lifeless.* **Iris** *talks to it, as if it were still alive.*

Iris: You shouldn't have done that, you really shouldn't. My mother was ever so upset. She says I ruined her party and she'll never forgive me. And she won't either! Why couldn't you keep your big mouth shut?

[**Mrs Jenkins** *sits with a handkerchief twisted in her lap*]

Mr Jenkins: Well, you must admit, she was different from Iris's other friends.

Mrs Jenkins: I was made a laughing stock. I don't know how I'm going to live it down. It'll be years before I dare give another party. We may even have to move.

Mr Jenkins: You know, there's a man here, who ...

Mrs Jenkins: Oh George, will you just shut up for once! [*She grabs his paper, tears it in shreds and scatters the pieces over his astonished head. While the paper is still fluttering down around* **Mr Jenkins***, the* **Postman** *appears outside the front door and rings the bell.* **Iris** *goes to answer it.*]

Postman: Is there something to be collected – return to sender?

Iris: Yes, in my room. [*She leads him to the doll*]

Postman: This one here? My goodness, is that a doll? It's amazing what they can do these days to make them look so lifelike. What's her name?

Iris: Siri.

Postman: Siri? That's unusual.

Siri: Hey, watch it now, fat face! Don't you start.

Postman: [*To* **Iris**] What did you say?

Iris: Nothing, nothing at all. It's quite all right.

Postman: OK then. Put the proper labels on, have you?

Iris: Yes – but here's an extra one, just to be safe. [*She writes 'Siri' in large letters on a label which she puts round the doll's neck. Then she suddenly notices something*] How odd! I've just noticed something. 'Siri' is my name written back to front. [*The*

Postman *carries the doll over his shoulder to the door.* **Iris** *calls after them*] 'Bye Siri. I must come to one of your parties some day.

Siri: Anything for a friend!

The end